THE ROBOT AND AUTOMATION ALMANAC 2020

THE FUTURIST INSTITUTE

Edited by Jason Schenker
Chairman of The Futurist Institute

THE ROBOT AND AUTOMATION ALMANAC - 2020

THE FUTURIST INSTITUTE

EDITED BY JASON SCHENKER

ISBN: 978-1-946197-37-5 *Paperback*
978-1-946197-36-8 *Ebook*

For futurists everywhere.

 THE FUTURIST INSTITUTE

CONTENTS

CONTENTS

CONTENTS

FROM THE FUTURIST INSTITUTE

On behalf of The Futurist Institute, I want to acknowledge and thank all of the contributors to *The Robot and Automation Almanac - 2020*. As in the past two years, we have an amazing cohort of contributors in the fields of robots, automation, and AI this year.

Thank you to Michael Walton, Brandon Coats, Carl Vause, Djamila Amimer, Erik Nieves, Ragu Athinarayanan, Grant Richards, Balamurugan Balakreshnan, Matt Wicks, Jason Gouw, Patrick Davison, Peter Bladh, Tom O'Donnell, Jeff Burnstein, Robert Huschka, Michael Field, Kaleb Steinhauer, Fred van Beuningen, Robert Handfield, Maxim Khabur, Russell Nickerson, Maciej Lisiecki, Łukasz Lipski, Daniel Stanton, and Nawfal Patel. I am humbled by this list of amazing authors!

The contributions of these leaders will help shape the vision for robots, automation, and AI in the year to come — and beyond. Their words and expectations for "the big thing" in the year ahead have created an important vision of the future.

Without them, this book would never have happened. Their visions of the future are both exciting and valuable.

I also want to thank parties who have helped out by providing recommendations for potential contributors, including MHI — the Material Handling Industry group — with which my financial market research firm, Prestige Economics, has a long-standing relationship.

Additionally, I need to thank the individuals who have provided support and feedback to this project, especially Nawfal Patel, who helped managed the process so that this book could come to fruition. And, of course, Kerry Ellis has my gratitude for designing such a wonderful cover for the almanac.

It is my personal pleasure to have been involved in this undertaking. The robotics, automation, and AI industries are still very new, but they are becoming more important. And it is with great pleasure that The Futurist Institute is able to support the companies in these industries with this almanac.

I founded The Futurist Institute to help strategists, analysts, and executives become futurists in October 2016; we recently began our fourth year of operations.

With the inaugural edition of *The Robot and Automation Almanac* in 2018, The Futurist Institute created an invaluable tool for professionals, individuals, and investors seeking to understand the implications of robots and automation for their personal, professional, and investing lives.

We have similarly high expectations for how *The Robot and Automation Almanac - 2020* will presage changes in the year ahead.

The transition from the information age into the automation age is underway. Thank you for being a part of this dynamic shift.

Welcome to the future! ~

Jason Schenker
Chairman of The Futurist Institute
Editor of *The Robot and Automation Almanac*

THE YEAR AHEAD AND BEYOND

Jason Schenker

- Chairman of The Futurist Institute -

Every year the topics of robots, automation, and artificial intelligence become more important. This is our third almanac on the subject, and the main themes of *The Robot and Automation Almanac – 2018* were that 2018 was going to be a critical year of transition, momentum, activity, investment, and technological potential. And we were going to see robots leave the factories and be everywhere.

In fact, that is very much how 2018 played out.

Going into 2019, our authors presented a view of a world in which robots and automation would make progress. And that 2019 was going to be a year in which AI and computational processing power would be increasingly important. Indeed, that is also how 2019 played out.

We are standing on the edge of the age of automation. What's next for robots and automation in 2020? This is the question that our contributors have answered in this book.

Going into 2019, there were also a couple of risks. On the one hand, 2019 was expected to be a year in which robots were forced to "slow down," according to Michael Walton, because of a need to wait for software to catch up with the robots. Indeed, software has made great strides, and Walton sees big expectations for a positive impact in 2020 — as do a number of our authors.

Another big potential challenge going into 2019 came from higher interest rates and trade risks. Indeed, interest rates caused growth and business investment to slow. And trade risks have increased.

There are also elevated concerns about the potential for tighter and stricter foreign investment allowed into the United States as part of stricter oversight and control by the Committee on Foreign Investment in the United States (CFIUS) going into 2019.

As we enter 2020, there are domestic and global macroeconomic risks. And the trade war continues. This could continue to weigh on business investment, including hindering some technological investments.

In the essays in this book, you will see a few different threads among the different authors.

In 2018, we divided *The Robot and Automation Almanac - 2018* into two parts: "Robots You See" and "Robots You Don't See." Then, in 2019, we divided our almanac into four sections: "Outlook for Robotics, Automation, and AI in 2019," "Socializing Robots," "Robots in Industry," and "Robots in the Supply Chain."

In the 2020 almanac, we see a few critical themes running through this book, including physical automation in controlled environments, a push for efficiencies, a march toward more effective operations, ethical challenges, environmental needs, and even the prospects for more automation with increased remote work.

In addition to their contributions, we are also grateful for all of the images our contributors granted us permission to use in this book.

The history of robots and automation is being written now.

In this book.

When people look back a decade from now, they will want to know how robots and automation evolved. They will want to understand how robots and AI became more integrated.

They will wish they had known more when it was happening.

They will wish they had read *The Robot and Automation Almanac* as it was happening. ~

Jason Schenker
Chairman of The Futurist Institute
Editor of *The Robot and Automation Almanac*

BIG LEAPS AHEAD IN 2020 FROM SOFTBOTS, EDGE DEVICES, AND FORM FACTORS

Michael Walton

- Microsoft Industry Solutions Executive -

There are big changes coming in the year ahead. Many of the hopes and promises for automation and softbot technology has not yet come to fruition. But in the year ahead, advances in artificial intelligence are likely to support three major leaps forward in technology — in softbots, edge devices, and form factors.

Softbots

The word "softbots" is a portmanteau for "software robots." In essence, this refers to software that facilitates automated activities of various kinds. Of course, we already have this kind of technology, but error rates have been high and data cleanliness problems have also been a major issue. These risks have diminished the potential impact of some previous attempts to implement softbots like robotic process automation — or RPA.

But in the year ahead, I see the potential for a rise of intelligent softbots. There is a potential for much greater success in automation by using improved artificial intelligence to reduce errors and improve overall quality control. This hope to automate the back end of operations is something that is high on the priority list for every company — in every vertical. This move to intelligent softbots can increase productivity while also lowering error rates and costs. And with AI, softbots can deliver on the past promises that have been unfulfilled. An additional important note is that Microsoft announced at its Ignite conference in 2019 that free AI RPA will be provided with Microsoft Flow.

I am excited about what this will mean for improving efficiencies in repetitive human work, especially in back-office activities like accounts receivable and accounts payable, as well as on the manufacturing production line. Plus, I am excited to see where AI will take us in the year ahead, as we see AI move to more complex activities that it will be able to perform at increasingly lower costs and with less effort. This is especially promising when we consider the potential to see AI increasingly integrate imagery, voice, sound, and other sources of data into process flow monitoring. This process will allow AI-supported softbots to collect increasingly meaningful data to develop insights and drive decision-making in real time.

Edge Devices
Another big change in the year ahead is likely to come from edge devices, which are devices that can directly collaborate with each other without intermediaries. In the year ahead, I expect to see big strides forward in this area.

Companies have been working hard for years to make as small as possible edge compute, which is the term for computing at the edge device level. This allows companies to take AI from the cloud — along with software — and put it on a local device. This prevents a disruption that occurs if cloud connectivity is lost.

In the year ahead, these edge devices that provide an entry into a network that fosters P2P interactions and uses AI will become much more commonplace. With localized decision-making ability and operability, devices will be able to make decisions at the machine level. And the supporting infrastructure can support how machines make decisions. Effectively, we are likely to increasingly have devices that can see all activities around them because edge devices allow for devices to connect with each other — and be responsive in the event of non-static incidents and changes. This also reduces the need for manufacturing execution systems (MES) because the devices themselves will be able to make decisions leveraging AI, softbots, and other software.

Of course, something similar to this can be done already with cloud computing. But the cloud presents single point of failure risks. And edge devices are likely to increasingly facilitate activities at the localized level (hybrid cloud). This needs to be operationally in a selected security stack, which means devices could operate at the device level or the plant level or even the multi-plant level. This means that edge devices still need industrial-grade security at the device level. This is why cloud security needs to exist at the device level — to secure intelligent devices. After all, intelligent and connected data needs security.

Form Factors

While AI and edge computing will facilitate big strides forward in the year ahead, improved form factors — more commonly known as engineering design — will also contribute significantly to a drive in automation use cases becoming pretty impressive.

Intelligent AGVs and intelligent drones will be increasingly ubiquitous in the year ahead. They will be monitoring inventories in warehouses and production lines in factories. But they will also be more commonly used to monitor farms, power lines, cell towers, and all kinds of businesses and infrastructure assets.

The drone devices in use will be increasingly more mobile — and they will be responsive to non-static situations. And devices are now 1/10th the size they were. They are safer and more agile, and they have greater access than ever before. With a greater ability to be deployed, drones will increasingly be able to offer real-time imagery and analyze real-time circumstances to predict needs.

AI, Automation, and Jobs

I have conversations every day about automation, robots, and AI. In every conversation, no one wants to replace people. There is a people shortage. And the war for talent has pushed companies to see automation as the only solution. This trend is likely to continue in the year ahead as technology becomes a critical level for companies — and workers — to boost their productivity. ~

Michael Walton is Director and Industry Solutions Executive at Microsoft, where he is helping discrete manufacturing companies to digitally transform.

FROM MANUAL TO LIGHTS OUT: A MATURING WAREHOUSE ROBOTICS MARKET

Brandon Coats

- Global Product Manager — Robotics of MHS Global -

Today's robotics solutions are more advanced than ever, capable of taking on more and more of the warehouse workload. Self-driving vehicles can move loads from point A to B, robotic arms can pick and place individual items, and still other robotic solutions can load and unload freight on the dock.

LogisticsIQ estimates the warehouse automation market will grow to $27 billion by 2025, up from $14 billion in 2019 — a compound annual growth rate of 11.7%.[1] This growth is powered by the intersection of key technology advances and major labor challenges.

The labor challenge boils down to this: businesses lack the staff necessary to handle the physical and repetitive tasks of the distribution center.

And the labor that is available is expensive and prone to high turnover.

But how high?

Depending on who you ask, the turnover rate for warehouse labor is in the neighborhood of 25%-36%.[2,3]

Turn the Lights Out and Productivity Up

As more solutions emerge to automate individual tasks, entire processes can eventually be handled with zero manual touches. Without the need for workers to navigate facilities, operations can literally turn the lights out and create a "dark" warehouse.

For example, to fully automate order fulfillment, robotic gripping technology can pick and place individual items, while an autonomous mobile robot can move inventory into position for picking and take away completed orders. This produces a complete order fulfillment cycle with no manual intervention.

Solutions like this that fully automate or even partially automate a process can greatly increase a warehouse's labor efficiency and significantly reduce headcount, thereby overcoming the labor shortage. Rather than a staff of hundreds engaging in repetitive, low value-added tasks, a smaller staff with a high level of technical skill would be required to keep operations moving.

But this also creates a new, "second wave" labor shortage.

Once businesses rely on automated systems, they must develop the technical skills to keep them up and running. While these jobs require significant training and institutional knowledge transfer, reassigning employees to these higher-level positions offers greater responsibility and a more pleasant work environment while drastically increasing the productivity of each individual employee.

Robotics and automation provide productivity multiples for each staff member while giving operators the super-human capability that industrial robots deliver. One problem that may emerge, however, is that traditional robotics platforms do not integrate well with collaborative efforts, nor do they lend themselves to an ease in programming or operation.

These critical pain points in the industry have led to the development of novel products that allow for high levels of collaboration between robots and staff while simultaneously reducing the effort required for programming.

As the market shifts to fill these gaps, it is anticipated that collaborative robots will merge with safe and redundant vision systems which allow robots to see, sense by touch, and anticipate the movements of surrounding objects and people. This will lead to improvements on the order of magnitudes in terms of flexibility in operations, as robot safety is driven to new levels of effectiveness and cages surrounding robots are made a factory relic of the past.

On the programming front, it is anticipated that the market will provide solutions that are natively programmed in software languages like Python. As programming languages eventually become as readable as English, training on robotics operating languages will become easier and faster.

When taken in conjunction with a drop in proprietary control languages and syntax, this change in programming language dynamics will enable robot adoption rates that can actually keep pace with rising market demand.

With the enabling technology changes well underway, it is reasonable to ask how far away a complete, lights-out operation is.

It's likely to be at least five years — and perhaps closer to 10 years — in the future. During that same timespan, though, the labor shortage is expected to become even more dramatic, with 2.4 million jobs estimated to go unfilled in manufacturing alone.[4] As such, end users are engaging trusted suppliers to leverage the power of the latest robotics technologies to develop new solutions for manual processes that have been long-standing targets for automation.

As for a truly lights-out operation, we can expect a reduction in labor per throughput demand on an order of magnitude, compared to traditional operations over the coming decade. We see the remaining labor operating collaboratively to reduce heavy lifting and repetitive tasks, while we also expect some labor to be retrained to shepherd a fleet of robots and keep them operational.

Handle Capacity Peaks with Pop-Up Facilities

While lights-out facilities are not currently on offer, the pop-up facility offers a heavily automated, flexible model. They are used by parcel carriers to bolster distribution capacity during peak periods, without the full investment of a permanent, fully staffed facility.

A pop-up facility can get online in about a month, provide extra cross-docking capacity for a couple months during peak season, then can be decommissioned in around the same time it took to get online.

The key to the extra cross-docking capacity in this setup?

A fleet of mobile robots.

As demographics shift geographies and online order volumes continue to grow, the pop-up facility model provides a leaner, more efficient solution for distribution networks to respond. And robotics offers a flexible, on-demand workforce ideal for redeployment and round-the-clock productivity during peak season.

Trust That Technology is Built for the Long Haul

Robotic technology continues to evolve and advance. And as new solutions hit the market in 2020, obsolescence can enter the discussion as operations scope out what's best for them. While current autonomous mobile robots commonly rely on 2D LiDAR technology, 3D navigation is actively in development and a growing market presence.

Should end users worry about robots they currently have deployed or on order?

The short answer is ... no.

Robot performance is not a zero-sum game. The increased performance of new advances does not come at the price of diminishing performance by existing units. Businesses can keep existing systems operating according to original specification and reap the expanded capabilities made possible by investments in more advanced sensors and processing power.

Start Down the Robotics Path
According to the 2019 MHI annual report, 32% of supply chain professionals report actively using robotics and automation.[5]

But in the context of the expected growth of the warehouse automation market described at the beginning of this article — expected to nearly double by 2025 — many operations are set to make their first foray into robotics in the coming years. As such, the market is beyond the awareness stage, now with an appetite for education on how to translate potential to practical value.

Getting started requires understanding how to harness the key benefits of modern robotic solutions. For autonomous mobile robots, their superior flexibility is key as they do not require guidance infrastructure to be laid out in order to function. This enables faster startup and easier reconfiguration, ideal for businesses that must regularly adapt to meet changing requirements.

But to deliver on the promise of flexibility, businesses must consider the human element. The user interface is critical to a smooth implementation, operation, and cultural acceptance of robotic systems. In today's connected world, people are accustomed to making a query for certain information through a web browser, then processing information through that interface. When managing robotic systems, users can request information from robots via a similar web browser-based interface that they already understand.

By capitalizing on existing familiarity with browsers, smartphone apps, and common work instructions, a strong user interface can allow operations to retrain scarce labor resources to monitor and run once-robotic systems.

Finally, businesses must set realistic expectations for the value a robotics investment can bring. It is critical to understand that a mobile robot cannot do everything alone — it must function as part of a broader system to drive real results. And one must be able to identify what key performance indicators are important to measuring success, such as rate requirements and a reduction in manual touches. With this understanding, it then becomes more obvious what tasks are the best candidates for automation, both immediately and years into the future.

By making a plan and taking a step-by-step approach to introducing automation, operations can create facilities with exceptional labor efficiency, order accuracy and more — whether it's technically a lights-out warehouse or not. ~

ENDNOTES

1. Source: https://www.roboticsbusinessreview.com/news/report-warehouse-automation-logisticsiq/
2. Source: https://www.huffpost.com/entry/making-friends-with-your-new-robot-co-worker_b_590c93bee4b0f711807243dd
3. Source: https://www.kaneisable.com/blog/top-challenges-of-managing-a-warehouse-staff
4. Source: https://www.pbs.org/newshour/economy/making-sense/manufacturers-say-their-job-shortage-is-getting-worse-heres-why
5. Source: https://www.supplychaindive.com/news/third-supply-chain-robotics--automation-cost-ROI-barrier/558290/

Brandon Coats is responsible for developing material handling systems that leverage robotics, sensors, machine vision, AI, and other exponential technologies.

CONSUMER-CENTRIC MANUFACTURING AND THE FUTURE OF ROBOTIC AUTOMATION

Carl Vause

- CEO of Soft Robotics -

The Fourth Industrial Revolution and Consumer-Driven Manufacturing

The fourth industrial revolution has ushered in a new consumer-driven manufacturing landscape. The consumer is truly king in this new world, where companies like Amazon have set a new standard for expectations around choice, control, convenience, and experience.

According to the World Economic Forum, globally, consumers have access to 1 billion different products. To keep pace with rising consumer expectations, manufacturers are tapping into new and novel approaches and technologies. Here we examine how dexterous, integration-ready, flexible robotic systems are addressing this monumental shift and paving the way for the factory of the future.

New Industries Turn to Automation for the First Time

There are several key drivers that are placing pressure on manufacturers to turn to robotic automation. Finding labor for repetitive, unskilled tasks like the picking and packing of goods has increasingly become a challenge, with manufacturer job postings up 280%, according to the Bureau of Labor Statistics. As labor continues to become scarcer, manufacturers are turning to automation to maintain their productivity, and in many cases, the economic viability of their product. An increase in consumers demanding more choices now has contributed to shorter product life cycles, shorter runs, and more line changes.

We've seen the transformative impact robotic automation has had on industries like automotive. Robots can increase throughput, accuracy, and consistency, all while decreasing worker-related accidents and safety hazards. For the packaging industry, robotic automation unlocks the flexibility needed to meet shorter product life cycles, new packaging designs, product variation, and batch manufacturing.

The challenge, however, is that traditional robots have been designed to perform a single task extremely efficiently. But when the item or the task changes, which is increasingly becoming the case in packaged goods, these traditional machines need to be reintegrated and reprogrammed, which can take hundreds of hours and significant capital investment.

This is why so many industries have been reliant on human labor — and the human hand specifically — to pick and pack their items.

The need for robots to solve for dexterous manipulation is stronger than ever. Even the U.S. government, in its 2016 *Roadmap for Robotics* report, cites "flexible gripping mechanisms that allow for dexterous manipulation of everyday objects" as a "national imperative."[1]

Robotic Automation is Reaching New Industries and Applications

Robotic automation was for decades limited to industries like automotive and electronics, where conventional, rigid robots were adept at automating non-variable production lines. Due to technological advancements and declining robot prices, however, robots are today reaching new industries and previously inaccessible applications.

One example of an emerging technology in this space is soft robotics, a new field out of Harvard University focused on the development of biologically inspired "soft robots" that are able to mimic the dexterity of the human hand. Traditional robotic manufacturers have attempted to replicate the human hand with rigid linkages, sensors, and sophisticated vision systems. Soft robotics' novel approach solves this problem through material science, not through higher levels of cost and complexity. Inspired by the octopus and its ability to manipulate objects, a soft robotic gripper is made entirely of soft materials that do not require sensors or other electromechanical devices for operation.

The computational power of the system is built into the gripper itself, a blend of materials with microfluidic channels that, when actuated, can manipulate items with human hand-like dexterity.

Enabling a Consumer-Centric Approach to Manufacturing

One of the greatest solutions to mounting consumer demands and SKU proliferation is innovations in the equipment on the factory floor. Here we examine how the dexterous, flexible, and collaborative nature of soft robotics is enabling CPG manufacturers to meet new market requirements.

Pick and Place Applications: Robotic automation is fantastic at applications that demand speed, precision, and repeatability. Products that are delicate and easily damaged have, until now, been primarily picked and packed off a conveyor belt by humans due to the risk of rigid grippers damaging the product. Soft robotic gripping solutions are able to maintain throughput requirements all while handling items with a "soft" touch. This opens up a multitude of new packaging possibilities for manufacturers.

Flexibility: With a single device, soft robotic grippers can handle an infinite number of products, without expensive and time intensive tool changes. This is especially important in the packaging space, where an ever-increasingly number of SKUs translates to constant product variation and new packaging designs.

Efficient Changeovers: The on-demand, modular nature of soft robotics enables faster, more efficient changeovers for manufacturers, lowering the threshold of volume and making robotic automation a more economical option for smaller batch sizes / niche tasks.

Not only can soft robotic grippers plug into all leading robotic arms, but the grippers themselves are modular, and can be quickly and easily adapted to meet the specific needs of the application.

The cost savings offered by this kind of low-volume automation will benefit many different kinds of organizations: smaller manufacturers will be able to access robotic technology for the first time, and larger ones could increase the variety of their product offerings.

Collaborating Safely with Workers: New workplace legislation and the need to reduce worker-related safety incidents are compelling reasons to make the move to robotic automation. Collaborative robots are designed specifically to work in close proximity to their human counterparts.

They can relieve workers of monotonous, tiring, and physical tasks, thereby increasing the quality and efficiency of human work. The soft materials used in the soft robotic gripper make it an excellent fit for collaborative applications. Soft Robotics has partnered with Universal Robotics to create a gripping system specifically tailored to collaborative robots and applications.

With the SRDK-UR+, users can quickly address an infinite number of applications, such as machine tending, high-speed packaging, pick and place, assembly and CNC machine automation.

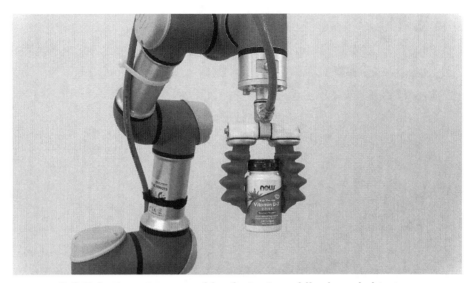
Soft Robotics gripper capable of gripping oddly shaped objects.

Conclusion

The pressure to meet constantly evolving consumer demands is creating new innovation in the packaging sector. Traditional industrial robotic systems were, until now, unable to handle packaging variability, personalization, and small batch sizes, forcing manufacturers to rely on human labor to perform complex processing tasks on small batches and premium packaging. With the introduction of soft robotics, manufacturers are able to unlock the transformative power of robotic automation to meet the needs of their customers. ~

ENDNOTES

1. Source: http://jacobsschool.ucsd.edu/contextualrobotics/docs/rm3-final-rs.pdf

Carl Vause is CEO of Soft Robotics, maker of gripping solutions that adapt to the supply chain without the cost and complexity of traditional robotic systems.

TOP ARTIFICIAL INTELLIGENCE APPLICATION AND TRENDS: 2020 AND BEYOND

Dr. Djamila Amimer

- CEO and Founder, Mind Senses Global -

Technology is changing the way we do business by making business operations more efficient and leveraging new opportunities.

The ultimate objective of AI is to enable machines to perform tasks such as problem-solving and decision-making. AI is an instrument that allows businesses to improve performance in several areas, such as cost reduction, margin improvement, market growth, and customer experience.

There has been a significant increase in terms of the number of businesses applying AI. AI adoption level has increased by 270% over the last four years.[1] According to McKinsey, AI will add $13 trillion to the global economy by 2030.[2] With no exception, all sectors will benefit from AI.

Key trends and applications for 2020 and beyond are as follows:

AI and Healthcare

The healthcare sector has seen the highest number of AI investments over the last three years. AI investments in healthcare are expected to continue to increase. The most promising AI applications include medical imaging and diagnosing, precision medicine, and drug discovery.

Currently, AI can detect patterns in medical imaging, thus enabling doctors to diagnose diseases such as cancer. With the advance of smartphone computing power and AI chips, image recognition is expected to enable future diagnosis at home for other type of illnesses.

AI and Finance

Financial services were ranked in the second position in terms of AI investments and deals. AI investments in this sector will continue to increase in the following areas: credit risk assessment, fraud detection, and trading. Robo-advisors are expected to manage around 10% of global investment assets by 2020.[3]

AI and Retail

The retail sector is expected to be the fastest adopter of AI, with 50% of retailers expected to adopt AI over the next three years.[4] Some of the exciting AI applications in retail include smart stores, personalized offerings, and the use of robots and drones to deliver goods to customers.

AI and Recruitment

AI deployed in recruitment is expected to increase in scope. In the past, AI applications were limited to CV analysis, keyword searches, and matching candidates to roles based on a set of criteria. However, with video interviewing, the use of AI is being shifted to analyzing human and personality traits together with candidates' emotions.

AI and Marketing

In the last few years, there have been several AI applications deployed in marketing such as targeted online campaigns. Looking forward, AI applications will continue to increase, particularly in the area of social listening and sentiment analysis and targeted advertising and content recommendations.

Social listening and sentiment analysis are crucial in detecting issues and resolving them. Companies can use AI to analyze social feeds and detect if there are any customers who might be unhappy with their products. On the other hand, targeted advertising and content recommendations are based on AI ability to cluster customer profiles and preferences.

AI and Virtual Assistants and Voice Search

AI assistants have found their way into managing our daily tasks. Nowadays there are millions of people using virtual assistants such as Google and Amazon's Alexa.

Virtual assistants are expected to make the leap from homes to workplaces, where businesses will be using AI assistants to automate repetitive work. Also, voice search is expected to be the most prominent area of virtual assistants, where searches are expected to increase by a third.

AI and Face Recognition and Surveillance

Face recognition applications have seen a significant deployment rate over the last couple of years. Nowadays we can see face recognition devices and software being deployed at airports and train stations for example.

Surveillance is an area that will benefit from the use of AI in terms of protecting our safety and detecting potential risks before they happen. But this is also an area that could infringe on privacy and personal liberties if the technology is not used in an ethical way and if there is no legal framework to govern procedures.

AI and Internet of Things

Internet of things (IoT) devices have the potential to generate a vast amount of data. However, data is only useful if we can act on its insights. Artificial intelligence is a good complement to IoT as it makes sense of the data collected through IoT, detects patterns, provides insights, and enables us to make decisions and adjust behaviors.

Useful applications of AI and IoT are in areas such as smart cities, autonomous driving, and smart home appliances.

AI and Blockchain

AI and Blockchain are two major technologies that have the potential to complement each other. On one hand, blockchains have usually high energy consumption and costs; artificial intelligence can help minimize energy consumption and optimize the data mining system. On the other hand, blockchain can help AI in terms of providing clearer audit trails and offering secure data sharing.

AI and Quantum Computing

Quantum computing has potential to dramatically accelerate the progress of artificial intelligence. The significant amount of computing power will enable AI and deep learning to potentially solve real big problems like climate change and incurable diseases.

AI for Good

AI applications for the "good" of humanity theme will continue to receive more attraction. Going forward, there will be continued efforts to align AI with United Nations Sustainable Development Goals.

We will see more AI applications in areas such as predicting earthquakes, dealing with natural disaster responses, protecting endangered species, detecting depression, and solving world hunger.

AI and Ethics and Transparency

Transparency and ethics will continue to be the main concerns surrounding artificial intelligence. Tightening laws and regulations, such as the General Data Protection Regulation (GDPR) have put pressure on AI developers and AI technologists to protect data but have also given the right "of explanation" to consumers to seek meaningful information about the logic involved in the AI algorithms.

With the slow response and progress in this area so far, there could be more regulations put in place to push for change. ~

ENDNOTES
1. Source: Gartner 2019 CIO Survey.
2. Source: McKinsey, AI frontier report, September 2018.
3. Source: World Bank, Robo-advisors, February 2019.
4. Source: xinhuanet.com, 15 January 2019.

Dr. Djamila Amimer is the CEO of Mind Senses Global, a boutique AI management consultancy that helps businesses and organizations apply AI and unlock its full potential.

COGNITIVE COLLABORATION: A ROBUST DEFINITION DRIVES PROGRESS

Erik Nieves

- Co-founder of Plus One Robotics -

Like all disruptive technologies must do after the initial enthusiasm of early adopters wanes, collaborative robots (cobots) are searching for their place in the broader robotics industry. To help them find it, we as their creators and beneficiaries must agree on a definition for this new technology. To date, we have — by default or design — defined collaborative robots as automated manipulators that operate safely enough to share a workspace with humans.

Cobots are commonly accepted as robots that "do no harm." If so, then we agree that the force-limited robot tending a CNC machine is a cobot. Likewise, the mobile robot navigating a hotel hallway to deliver fresh towels or replace a forgotten toothbrush is also a cobot. Yet when compared with the robust cooperation implied by the word "collaborative," a definition focused exclusively on safe proximity hollows out the fullness inherent in the word.

I believe that a "safety only" definition of collaborative does a disservice to the word and places a limit on the number of applications suitable for automation.

Think for a moment about factory employees on a production line. If two people spend the day working side by side and both go home that night physically unharmed by the other, we would not say that the absence of injury constitutes collaboration. However, if the two have interacted, have exchanged information, and have contributed their respective strengths to accomplish a production task, we would reasonably label their efforts "collaborative."

Further, we recognize that collaboration can take various forms. If one person asks another for instruction and receives the requested information, if one picks up the slack for the other, or if two decide to divide the workload, then we can agree that collaboration has taken place. We recognize that the word "collaborative" encompasses an exchange of information and a cooperative effort for the purpose of accomplishing a common goal.

In the context of the growing collaborative robotic industry, it is useful to think about the types of play that children engage in as they mature. Sociologist Mildred Parten recognized discrete patterns of behavior and labeled them "stages of play."[1] She observed that infants and young children engage in solitary play, a stage where they are absorbed with their own play process, both unaware and uninterested in those playing around them.

Solitary play might be likened to the traditional industrial robot that toils away, indifferent to the fact that it is safely locked in a cage. As children begin to watch others play, they mature into parallel play, generally a preschool stage where children are aware of each other but there is no interaction between them. In this stage, we may see two children driving cars across the carpet, knowing they have a friend beside them but uninvolved with each other. Parallel play is analogous to the developmental stage of today's cobots: safe proximity.

As parents we do not want our children to get stuck in the stage of parallel play. If by kindergarten or first grade we have not seen our children begin to play cooperatively, we become alarmed. Cooperative play is the stage when children begin to communicate with each other, organizing their activity and performing assigned roles to achieve a mutual goal.

It is during cooperative play that we observe collaborative behavior. By any common measure, collaboration is always understood to be more cognitive than a mere "do no harm" definition allows. And it is this cognitive, interactive definition of collaboration that is the next stage of development for cobots.

Already existing in a limited number of labs and in pockets of industry, cognitive collaboration between humans and cobots will become widespread in the next ten years. During this decade we will see humans and cobots dividing work and assigning roles based on capabilities.

The cobot is going to do what it is good at, the people what they are good at. The cobot will bring its power, speed, repeatability, and endurance to the task, while the people will bring their senses, thinking, and decision-making skills. Humans and cobots will build contingencies between them, allowing the cobot to work steadily until it runs into a problem and has to ask its human partner for help. True collaboration — cognitive collaboration — will allow people to do more than labor beside cobots. It will allow them to engage with cobots to accomplish tasks that had previously been inaccessible to automation.

The mechanism by which cognitive collaboration will be accomplished is termed "supervised autonomy." This means that we let the cobot do the work it can, of its own volition, to the degree possible. But when the cobot encounters an unexpected situation, an edge case, a human supervisor is present to jump in and assist until the cobot can work autonomously again. In some applications, there is a high degree of autonomy on the part of the cobot, but the cobot's work is improved or managed by including a human in the loop for those occasions when the cobot has reached the limits of its abilities.

In our work at Plus One Robotics, we employ supervised autonomy to manage the inherent variability of warehouse tasks. Unlike the cobot loading a million copies of the same part into a CNC, a fulfillment center cobot must handle a million distinct SKUs. For many years the sheer variety of shapes, colors, and materials has been a barrier to automating warehouse piece picking.

Supervised autonomy, however, is successfully breaking that barrier, bringing in cobots to do dull but necessary tasks that previously only humans had been capable of performing. Better than 95 percent of the time, a cobot can handle the work, picking and sorting pieces autonomously. But when it runs into a problem, the cobot can signal its remote human supervisor, who is capable of quickly assessing the situation and telling the cobot what to do. Cognitive collaboration bridges the gap between the limitations of machines and the capabilities of humans, allowing cobots to become valuable partners in this rapidly growing industry.

Many roboticists are laboring feverishly to fully automate warehouses and other centers of production. While full automation is an attractive goal, logic as well as our experience says that this target has more appeal than practicality. Complete robotic autonomy requires the meticulous structuring of a robot's environment so that it can operate with zero unexpected events. Unfortunately, there is no such Shangri-La in the warehouse or in the factory — or on the tarmac either. Remember the image of that out-of-control beverage cart swinging wildly in circles, nearly running over employees and careening closer and closer to a parked airplane? Jorge Manalang, a ramp instructor, commandeered another vehicle and crashed into the rogue cart. Manalang's ingenuity and quick thinking prevented serious damage to people or aircraft.[2] Human decision making will always be needed when the unexpected happens — and sooner or later, it always happens. Cognitive collaboration allows work to flow efficiently and prevents the unexpected from stopping production.

It's not that the definition of collaborative as "safe to work beside" is inaccurate; it is simply that in the labor-strained markets across many industries, safety is not enough. Future growth of the robotics industry requires a richer definition of collaboration.

The markets with a high degree of repeatability have already been automated. A shrinking pool of willing or available labor means that markets characterized by high variability are eager for the advantages that automation offers.

The only way to meet this need is for us to embrace the idea that cobots are better when they can rely on people to make the tough decisions. Cobots need us and always will. Through cognitive collaboration, cobots will find a firm place at the growing edge of our industry, where they can bring the full advantages of automation to markets that will always rely on human ingenuity. ~

ENDNOTES

1. Source: https://www.canr.msu.edu/news/the_power_of_play_part_1_stages_of_play
2. Source: https://www.usatoday.com/story/travel/airline-news/2019/10/01/american-airlines-envoy-employee-details-catering-truck-incident/3833327002/

Erik Nieves co-founded Plus One Robotics to bring industrial robotics to the warehouse through the development of 3D machine vision and supervised autonomy.

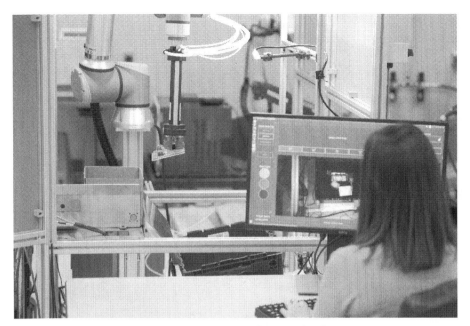

Plus One Robotics collaborative robot working with a human supervisor

THE DEMOCRATIZATION OF COMPUTING AND MANUFACTURING EVOLUTION INTO THE ERA OF ARTIFICIAL INTELLIGENCE

Ragu Athinarayanan, Grant Richards, Michael Walton, Balamurugan Balakreshnan

- Purdue University and Microsoft Corporation -

The 4th Industrial Revolution (IR4.0) is fundamentally changing the way we live and work, blurring boundaries between humans, physical systems, and the digital world. This paradigm shift is possible through the digital transformation strategies of "Making All Things Digital," "Making All Things Smart," and "Making all Things Connected." Enabled by the Internet of Things (IoT), data, and Artificial Intelligence (AI), this transformation is expected to impact business, industries, and economies through structural process changes occurring at unprecedented speed.

For manufacturing, in particular, this digital transformation will introduce a vast array of new opportunities for increasing efficiency, lowering costs, improving quality, and allowing production systems to achieve higher levels of operational effectiveness.

A report by McKinsey & Company published in 2017 shows the manufacturing sector has the potential to see a 20%-50% reduction in cost for inventory holding, a 10%-20% reduction in costs due to quality issues, a 45%-55% increase in productivity, and a 30%-50% reduction in total machine downtime when using IoT and data-driven strategies in manufacturing. Another key finding from NIST's economic analysis study conducted in October 2016 shows how manufacturers in the United States could save $57.4 billion annually through the effective use of data.

Small and medium-sized enterprises, including large corporations, accumulate vast amounts of data from their operations; however, data utilization remains very low at less than 6% nationally. Most manufacturing organizations do not have a proven strategy for purposeful collection and utilization of data. Additionally, they often lack access to tools for analyzing data they collect. One of the many outcomes of IR4.0 and the digital transformation is the democratization of computing through the use of cloud technologies.

With the democratization of computing and the availability of technologies such as cloud computing, manufacturers will soon be able to use techniques of computational science on the data they collect. Cloud computing tools will also enable them to create intelligence from their systems by discovering hidden patterns and extracting information from their data. Cloud technology will transform the way industries build and deploy solutions, which today require highly trained development teams.

With the expansion of cloud computing platforms from providers such as Microsoft, Google, and Amazon, computing capabilities will become more accessible to manufacturers of any size and budget. Through this democratization of scalable computing, small and medium enterprises (SMEs) will have access to the tools necessary to become more competitive and drive more innovation in manufacturing.

The democratization of AI is quickly becoming a prime focus for cloud computing companies seeking to provide manufacturers with the right set of building blocks for developing functional solutions using AI. This ever-increasing accessibility to high technology tools provides a pathway to allow for applications of Artificial Intelligence (AI), which will soon become one of the most disruptive technologies of the IR4.0 manufacturing revolution. The manufacturing sector can lead the way in the application of AI focused on optimizing processes, improving efficiency, productivity, and quality, as well as improving the safety of employees.

The United States currently holds an industrial output totaling over $3.602 trillion of an annual GDP of $18 trillion. A recent study conducted by PricewaterhouseCoopers (PwC) shows the global GDP could be 14% higher by 2030 as a result of AI adoption, equivalent to a contribution of $15.7 trillion to the global economy.

According to this report, the greatest economic gains from AI will be in China (26% boost to GDP in 2030) and North America (14.5% boost), for a combined total of $10.7 trillion and accounting for almost 70% of the global economic impact.

In the United States, industrial AI's impact on manufacturing appears in five primary areas. The first is in maintenance/OEE, specifically predictive maintenance, which has become a very sought-after use case for manufacturers. Applying AI to status and trend data from critical machinery and processes enables the accurate prediction of parameters such as End-of-Life (EoL) and Remaining Useful Life (RUL) of machines and their parts, as a means of optimizing OEE, minimizing unscheduled downtimes, and scheduling maintenance and repairs at the best point in time without unnecessary interruptions.

Second, the rising complexity of products and continued shrinking of time to market goals produces an environment where AI will have a significant impact on maintaining consistently high levels of quality in production. An expanding portfolio of industrial sensors can inform AI solutions focused on spotting early indicators of production problems and potential failures before they occur, which can save manufacturers resources and time, reduce scrap, and maintain the quality standards of their production systems. Additionally, AI solutions can be developed to improve product and process quality through the continual sampling of performance data from machinery and processes in the field, extending to the raw material quality in the supply chain.

Third, AI will play an important role in ensuring manufacturing robots can work safely and efficiently alongside humans, allowing for improved workplace safety and health benefits as workers transition from activities that are risky or prone to repetitive motion injuries to those focused on more advanced functions. AI will enable robots to tackle basic cognitive tasks and make autonomous decisions based on real-time environment data providing the core technology in developing this capability on modern factory floors.

Fourth, AI will change the way products are designed and bring significant improvements to the product design life cycle. Using AI algorithms, designers and engineers can now use generative design software to explore possible novel design configurations constrained by such things as weight, physical dimensions, material types, production methods, budget limitations, etc. This new approach will revolutionize manufacturing by enabling human engineers to define an engineering problem solved through an AI-driven generative design software program.

Fifth, AI will provide decision-making capability for optimizing manufacturing supply chain operations. Using AI tools and Big Data, manufacturers can develop analytic models to predict market demands by looking for patterns informed by consumer behavior, socioeconomic and macroeconomic factors, location, weather, and more. By anticipating these market changes, manufacturers will be able to use this information to optimize their supply chain, regulate raw material inventory, manage production levels, and staffing.

The democratization of computing will soon lead to the democratization of AI in manufacturing, which will eventually result in AI skill shortages. David Vasko, Director of Advanced Technology at Rockwell Automation, said, "There's a lack of AI-related skills in the marketplace; demand for data and AI skills will continue to outstrip supply." U.S.-based manufacturers need to prepare for the proliferation of new types of AI-related jobs in manufacturing. ~

The authors, in a partnership between Purdue University and Microsoft Corporation, are jointly developing Intelligent Manufacturing curricula for the present and future workforce.

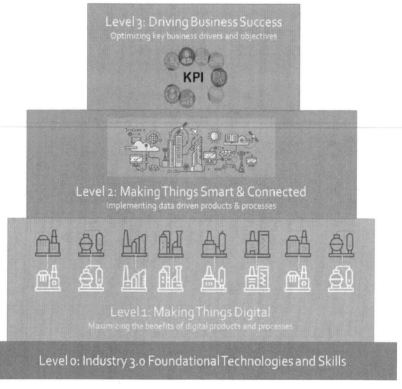

Image source: PTC

THE ROBOTS ARE COMING TO SAVE YOUR COMPANY

Matt Wicks

- Chief Robotics Solution Architect at Honeywell Intelligrated -

Automation Will Ease Burdens for Employers and Workers

Many tasks that were once considered impractical for robots are not only possible today, but they're well on their way to becoming routine. This is not the result of a single innovation but of many. Robotics control, machine learning, artificial intelligence (AI), computer vision, autonomous mobility, and gripping technologies have all made significant strides in the last few years alone. Cost factors are no less significant.

As these technologies have matured, they've become more affordable to a wider range of potential users. While these advances are enabling a new generation of smart robotics to move beyond traditional limitations, they're also shifting the workforce into jobs that are more uniquely suited for people to perform.

Fortunately for both workers and their employers, today's automation trends have a strong potential to benefit everyone. There are encouraging signs, both in the coming year and further out, that robots are far less likely to replace people than to improve their overall job prospects.

At the World Economic Forum in 2018, for example, it was estimated that by the year 2022, AI and robotics will create almost 60 million more jobs than they'll eliminate.

Signs of this shift are already visible in many industries, from manufacturing to e-commerce and distribution. We're even starting to see automated innovations in a few retail chains as they step up their games to compete with online giants.

These trends are likely to gain momentum in 2020, suggesting that the time is ripe for a new automation paradigm. Far from replacing their human counterparts, robots are becoming their co-workers and collaborators — creating new opportunities for productivity, accuracy, cost savings, and job satisfaction. As beneficial as these improvements are in and of themselves, changing consumer expectations will make them critical to the survival of many operations.

The Real Threat

One of the most significant threats to retailers is the growing demand for many businesses, especially in logistics and distribution, to keep up with the exponential growth of e-commerce and the constant pressures to drive down costs.

In fact, it could be argued that any operation that wants to remain competitive in the face of today's changing marketplace will soon find automation critical to its very survival.

Disruptive changes to commerce are the cause. The internet has revolutionized the way we buy just about everything, accelerated by the widespread adoption of smartphones. New parents, for example, can compare the cost of infant shoes among multiple retailers in just a few clicks. Nearly every product has become commoditized. What's more, retailers no longer compete just within a local town or region but potentially face rivals anywhere in the world. At the same time, e-commerce customers have been trained to expect superior service and shipping at little or no cost.

E-commerce has now evolved far beyond the days when it was a novelty used only by the young or tech-savvy early adopters. Transaction volumes continue to expand significantly each year. This in turn accelerates annual demands on distribution channels by around 25 percent.

Scarce Workers Limit Productivity

As if these pressures weren't challenging enough, every player in the chain is struggling with a significant labor shortage. Industry growth continues to outpace available workers by a factor of six to one.

Even though today's labor shortage was predicted almost a decade ago, many companies were caught unprepared. Roughly 10,000 baby boomers have reached retirement age every day since 2011, and there are fewer younger workers available to replace them. Both trends are set to continue for more than a decade. Departing workers are also leaving behind significant gaps in both skills and anecdotal knowledge traditionally learned on the job.

Eighty-four percent of warehouses attempting to hire new employees report there are few qualified applicants — or worse, none at all. In the United States alone, 600,000 warehouse jobs went unfilled in 2017. Turnover rates as high as 36 percent and rising wage growth drive costs even higher.

In this environment, automation poses little threat to the jobs of individual workers. Even if robotic co-workers are deployed on a large scale in the coming years, there are likely to be more jobs available than there are qualified people to fill them for many years to come.

Even unskilled laborers can outperform robots in many tasks. Basic cognition and our senses give humans the abilities to comprehend their surroundings, make informed decisions, react quickly to change, and move effortlessly through chaotic environments. Practically without thinking, they can function in ways robots are only beginning to approximate with their sophisticated algorithms and software. Humans also combine the strength to lift heavy objects with an instinctive ability to use just the right amount of grasping force.

Yet despite these mental and physical advantages, humans aren't always the best choice for some tasks. Robots provide an obvious and beneficial alternative, not as replacements, but as a means to free up scarce human brainpower for higher-value tasks.

Leveraging Productivity

The most significant opportunities for automation today are in jobs where robots can reduce or eliminate the risks of injury, overexertion, repetitive motion, and discomfort. Jobs like these tend to be the most difficult to fill, with some of the highest rates of turnover and absenteeism. By taking on the tasks, humans are less suited or willing to perform, robotics can augment available labor to achieve higher levels of productivity.

For example, a single human worker with minimal training can oversee multiple robotic unloaders for trucks, trailers and shipping containers, eliminating a common bottleneck while minimizing product damage, worker injuries, and exposure to extreme seasonal temperatures.

In a similar way, a picker can rely on a mobile robotic "partner" to convey products. This boosts productivity by enabling the human to spend more time finding items in an ever-changing warehouse environment and less time walking from place to place.

The New Automation Paradigm

A cutting-edge combination of superior vision, high-speed onboard intelligence, sophisticated gripping technology, and other allied components now enables robots to perform tasks that could previously be handled only by manual labor. At the same time, machine learning and AI are enabling robots to perform more complex operations. In connected operations, robots are also adapting quickly to changing conditions, like new packaging or product types. And once a single robot learns the solution to a new challenge, its training model can be pushed out to robots throughout an entire operation, even to multiple sites worldwide.

Automation's advantages offer an increasingly attractive resource for relieving human labor from dull, dirty, and dangerous tasks, freeing scarce workers for more satisfying roles. In addition, strategic collaborations between humans and robots can create opportunities for efficiency and productivity that exceed what either can accomplish on their own. ~

Matt Wicks has 25 years of experience in the material handling industry, with expertise in controls, software integration, and advanced robotic solution development for manufacturing and distribution systems. He holds a bachelor's degree in Electrical Engineering from the University of Missouri–Rolla and serves as second Vice Chair on the Robotics Industry Association Board of Directors.

Honeywell's robotic unloader

STEAM EDUCATION: GREATER THAN THE SUM OF ITS PARTS

Jason Gouw

- Founder of Cubit -

T minus 5.. 4.. 3.. 2.. 1.. 0.. ..an eerie pause followed by the crisp ignition of a rocket engine propels what looks like a 39-meter-tall stainless-steel water tower into the sky before yawing in flight and descending with perfect precision to the center of its landing zone. On August 27, 2019, SpaceX made a successful 150-meter test flight of its Starhopper vehicle. A technology test that SpaceX hopes to evolve for transporting humans to Mars someday.

I was lucky enough to watch the live video feed during the test on August 27, and it was one of the most exciting rocket launches I have seen — even with a flight time of less than 60 seconds and achieving an altitude of 150 meters (hardly worth mentioning in the rocket world). What some may not realize is the number of breakthroughs SpaceX achieved in the Starhopper project: knowledge from a wide variety of subjects and backgrounds.

Without applying the fields of material science, robotics, physics, and computer science, Starhopper would not have been possible. SpaceX, like many companies in the tech industry, utilizes the power of *knowledge transference* — combining information and knowledge from a wide variety of subjects and backgrounds.

To better prepare our young people in an integrated-information future, K-12 education and STEM companies have realized the importance of integration and are trying to implement better integrated approaches to STEM education. Traditionally, STEM has had a very siloed approach covering only one or two subjects at best — typically coding and robotics.

Briefly going back to SpaceX and the importance of information integration, here are examples of some of the areas that SpaceX mastered in order to achieve success in the Starhopper flight test:

Material Science was necessary in the design of the unique rocket engine configuration dubbed the "Raptor." Unlike most rocket engines, the Raptor uses oxygen and methane as fuel in a very rare full-flow-staged-combustion configuration. This rocket configuration poses great challenges, necessitating SpaceX to develop new metals that can withstand the extreme heat and pressure within certain parts of the rocket engine. Why, might you ask, would SpaceX choose such a challenging non-traditional design at the cost of more resources and time? The main reasons have to do with fuel efficiency, maximizing thrust-to-weight ratios, and achieving reusability of over 50x to make transportation to Mars a possibility from a technological and economical standpoint.

Robotics systems for vectoring the single-nozzle rocket at the bottom of Starhopper for total control in three-dimensional space. Imagine balancing a pencil on your finger by its tip to lift, maneuver, and land without the pencil wobbling or toppling over!

Data Science to process millions of sensor inputs per second and correlate understanding to what they mean.

Computer Science for calculating projections and possibilities, learning, and providing the optimal decision and instructions for the spacecraft at any given time.

These are only a few examples of the wide breadth of subjects and topics needed for SpaceX's mission.

The K-12 education industry, unlike most startups, is a very slow-moving ship. Schools and districts are often inundated by organizational structure challenges, budget timing, and day-to-day challenges of classroom management. Add to that state and federal standards requirements, regulations, and changing policies, the education sector often finds itself trying to push through a gridlock — acknowledging the necessity for change but unable to respond quickly. Progress in this field is slow but does eventually happen.

Several years ago, there was a big boom in STEM-related products. There were many companies and startups that produced various types of small, programmable robots.

These robots were relatively easy to use — not much assembly was required, if any, and programming was done through an easy-to-use visual-programming interface. Instructions served more as activity guides than educational curricula, but the little robots got kids engaged and teachers loved having a classroom of engaged students. The problem is that engagement does not always mean efficacy. In the case of these "educational toys" marketed as STEM platforms, kids didn't really learn that much, if any, in terms of engineering, science, or math. What they did learn was to follow activity instructions and to have fun.

School districts bought into this idea for a few years, implementing a large number of these robot kits into their schools to boost their STEM programs. They soon realized that these products only delivered some educational value in the computer science field and not much else. It was challenging for schools to fit such product into anything other than a robotics or engineering class — elective classes that did not have standard requirements and were not offered at every school. Science and math classes, on the other hand, are offered in almost every grade level and at every school, but since these classes had specific state requirements and standards to achieve, the programming focus of the robot kits was of little value.

Within the span of just the last few months, however, there have been large pivots from several of these educational toy companies to focus more on actual learning value within the STEM field. The robot kits have evolved with additional hardware and sensors that allow more applications into the realm of science and engineering.

Students can now collect sensor data from the environment to influence different robot interactions and apply more science-based projects with the robots. Curricula based on these robots were created for each grade level, often extending into the science area and achieving a few of the required science and math standards. Though most of the science- and math-related projects are somewhat contrived and stretched the capabilities of the robots, it does show the response STEM education companies are making to fulfill the need for a more integrated STEM approach in the classroom.

Larger companies have also made pivots to offer a more integrated platform. Lego's robotics kits have traditionally been very boy-centric, with activity guides for assembling aggressive-looking robots. Since recent times, they've released robot kits that are design friendly for both boys and girls while adding features that allow application into the math and science classrooms. An example from the other side of the spectrum is Vernier Software and Technologies, a brand most often used in classroom science labs for its scientific and test equipment. Though Vernier does not produce any robotic type kits, they offer more science instruments that incorporate technologies that allow them to be integrated with engineering and technology classes.

It is a very exciting time to see how schools will respond to the new wave of integrated STEM products and if schools, in turn, will evolve to offer more integrated classrooms to produce better thinkers and problem solvers for the opportunities of tomorrow. ~

Jason Gouw and his brother grew up with a father that engaged them with hands-on projects made from scraps. Jason grew up to teach himself electronics and robotics and started his own design firm at 18, where he prototyped custom electronics for various companies such as GE and Hallmark. In 2014, he started Cubit, a STEAM education company for K-12 education. He hopes to bridge what he's learned in the industry and bring it into the way we educate our kids about the future of technology.

AUTOMATION IN MATERIAL HANDLING: THE RISE OF THE WAREHOUSE ROBOTS

Patrick Davison

- Director of Standards of MHI -

In 2019, MHI, a trade association whose members represent the material handling industry, launched The Robotics Group, an industry group whose mission is to inspire confidence and foster the adoption of robotic solutions to drive efficiency in supply chain applications.

Despite the group being new, automation in supply chain solutions has been implemented for decades. Industrial robots have been deployed for palletizing and depalletizing, bin picking, and various loading and unloading applications.

Automated guided vehicles (AGVs), automated storage and retrieval systems (AS/RSs), and more recently autonomous mobile robots (AMRs) have been widely deployed in the material handling applications.

Changes in consumer expectations, labor, and technology are affecting the material handling industry. The "Amazon effect," or disruption in the retail market resulting from e-commerce, is putting more of an onus on distribution centers to fulfill consumer demand. Low unemployment is putting wage pressure on warehouse workers, who can demand a higher salary. On the technology front, the deployment of collaborative robotic applications, improved end-of-arm tooling, and reliable sensors have paved the way for robotics and automation to take on tasks in warehousing distribution that would have been unthinkable just a few years ago. The manifestation of these trends makes it conceivable to imagine that more and more tasks in warehousing and distribution will be administered robotically.

This concept is not new. During the rise of robots in manufacturing in the 1970s and 1980s, we found that the so-called manual "D" tasks — dull, dirty, or dangerous — were taken over by robots. The robots deployed in assembly lines of yore were often super-human in their capabilities. Their speeds, precision, stamina, and payloads were superior to their human counterparts. A typical deployment in the 1990s or early 2000s would involve robots with a payload capacity of 50 kilograms or more, and their size and power required them to be isolated from workers with fencing or other protective barriers.

In the past ten years, a whole industry segment of robots with capacities of 10 kilograms or less have blossomed on the marketplace, and many of those have intrinsic power- and force-limiting capabilities that enable them to work safely alongside people.

These new robots are capable of ever more tasks that replicate human activity, including an increasing number of tasks in material handling applications.

It is important to note the vast differences between a manufacturing assembly line and a distribution center to realize the automation deployment challenges that lie ahead in the distribution space. Interchangeable parts, first introduced in the late 18th century, were fostered through the 19th-century Industrial Revolution and the assembly line in the early 20th century, which helped to enable the deployment of the first industrial robot in 1961. Robots in manufacturing rely upon precision parts assembled to exacting details on a highly controllable timeline and were the product of centuries of incremental technological improvements.

Distribution centers work on an entirely different paradigm. They can, at best, make educated guesses at what their next item to handle will be. Variability leads to complexity, and complexity increases cost. Automation deployments are most effective, including most cost-effective, when the solution can focus on a specific task. Any process change, be it physical or temporal, can hinder the opportunity for an automation project to succeed.

In contemplating automation applications in material handling, it is important to understand what material handling is. At MHI, we define material handing as "the movement, protection, storage and control of materials and products throughout manufacturing, warehousing, distribution, consumption and disposal."

Our members manufacture conveyors, racks, lifts, shelves, and a host of other equipment. That equipment, in turn, is used in movement, protection, storage, and control applications. I often think of material handling as being about the verb and not the noun. Material handling is not about the *thing*; it is about what the thing *does*.

A fundamental first step in contemplating any automation project is to consider all the tasks or activities being implemented to achieve a desired outcome. Ask yourself, "What needs to be done?" A deep dive to assess tasks and associated details is critical. The more defined tasks, the better; for when the tasks are fully described, they can then be analyzed to determine the most practical method for its achievement, be it manual, automated, or automated with a human in the loop. There now exist a myriad of off-the-shelf solutions that address increasingly specific tasks. For example, an MHI member who produces sortation and packing solutions utilizes machinery in their system that automatically presents and opens an envelope to a human operator, who can then stuff the opened envelope more rapidly. Who among us hasn't dealt with the inconvenience of an envelope that wouldn't open? If the task list for the packing process did not include a task as mundane as "OPEN ENVELOPE," the deployment of this solution could have been missed.

An additional thought on the concept of who does what is the notion that, while the promise of technology involves the ability to do an increasingly larger number of tasks with machines, there are several tasks that humans will still be able to do better ... at least for the foreseeable future.

I like to suggest the mental exercise of asking whether a given task would be more easily performed by a ten-year old child or a state-of-the-art machine built in a leading R&D laboratory. Activities such as finding a red ball in a toy box, opening a door, or avoiding an obstacle are second nature to a child but are extremely complex for a machine. Conversely, administering complex algorithms, following precise instructions, or conducting repetitive tasks without error would be a breeze for a simple computer but nearly impossible for a child. Playing to the strengths of both people and machines only makes sense. Nearly a half century after the deployment of robots in manufacturing, we still see people on an assembly line. Robots augment and supplement, but not always substitute, human labor. It would stand to reason that we will continue to need people in material handling applications, even after automated solutions have been implemented.

In material handling applications, order picking is still perceived as the most difficult task to automate. As an example, let's consider the same ten-year-old on a shopping trip with her parents. She would find it easy to select a shirt, a scooter, and a box of cereal from the store shelves and put it in her parents' shopping cart. Conversely, our R&D engineers building a specialized machine would likely find that the variability of sizes, weights, substrates, and other factors pose a formidable challenge. Now imagine a shopping experience where a filled cart is autonomously delivered to a checkout station where automated payment processing is implemented, thereby avoiding the time and frustration of long cashier lines.

If we think of a distribution center as a large shopping market, such an experience could be a reality. We could deploy people to pick orders, since that is difficult for machines, but then allow machinery to administer the order distribution and final processing experience, which would be tedious for the employee. Win-win!

This raises the big question: Can material handling operations adopt processes, such as assembly lines, that could simplify the complexity of distribution center operations and make them more amenable to automation? Or will technologists need to build better perception, manipulation, and mobility into their machines (i.e., making them more humanlike), in order to address the complex tasks associated with distribution center operations? In other words, an automated future in material handling will rely either on improved processes, improved technology, or a combination of both.

How will automation affect employment? Will robots take people's jobs? The deployment of automated teller machines (ATMs) at banks offers another insight into a possible material handling future. ATMs were able to process simple transactions, such as deposits, withdrawals, and balance inquiries, which in turn meant that fewer bank tellers were needed to operate a branch office. Rather than finding a slew of bank tellers in the unemployment line, banks realized they could deploy more branch offices since the operational labor expense of a branch office decreased with the presence of the ATM. New branch offices opened, requiring an increased need for bank tellers.

It stands to reason that a reduction in the labor expenses for material handling applications will result in the deployment of more distribution centers, perhaps with a specialized purpose or function, resulting in an increased demand for distribution center workers.

Several veteran MHI members claim they've never seen the current level of interest and excitement in the material handling industry, and the promise of automation in material handling applications is a cause for the excitement. Technology advancements are creating ever more opportunities, and the pace of change has never been faster. The ever-evolving landscape means we will likely have two new challenges for every challenge we solve, but for now, the future looks bright.

Patrick Davison is the Managing Executive of The Robotics Group and Director of Standards for MHI. He was formerly the Director of Standards Development for the Robotic Industries Association and a project manager at FANUC Americas.

CONVERGENCE OF DRIVERLESS VEHICLES IN INTRALOGISTICS

Peter Bladh

- Director of Product Management of Kollmorgen -

According to the International Federation of Robotics (IFR), the market for industrial robots has been growing at a record rate of 19% since 2012 and is forecast to continue to grow at a double-digit pace through to 2021. The segment of driverless vehicles — automated guided vehicles and autonomous mobile robots (AGVs and AMRs) — is growing fast, with 69,000 units installed in the logistics sector during 2017 and a further 600,000 units expected to be installed by 2021.

Beyond production costs, the main driving forces behind the rapid growth differ among different industries, according to the report Industrial Robotics, by McKinsey & Company, from 2019. Automotive companies invest in robotics to improve flexibility and safety for employees, electronics companies to improve quality and productivity, and pharmacological companies to improve quality and production capabilities.

The rapid expansion is of course very exciting and leads to a lot of opportunities within multiple applications. But it also constitutes challenges as regards the integration and streamlining of logistics processes, which many end users discover when they are about to scale up from small proofs of concept and pilots to larger installations. And these challenges increase when companies deploy automation globally.

Driving Factors

The increasing awareness of sustainability issues within the booming e-commerce sector and the automotive industry has put focus on the need to optimize the use of scarce and expensive production resources. Concepts such as smart warehouses and smart factories have been developed, which has led to the development of a plethora of AMRs and AGV types such as piggybacks, towing vehicles, unit load vehicles, forklift trucks, high-reach trucks, and purpose-built AGVs. The fastest growing segments are AMRs and forklift AGVs. They are a powerful addition to manufacturing companies because they increase the number of value-adding tasks that can be performed and reduce the number of dangerous and repetitive operations for employees. They are also the first step towards a more complete automation of the entire flow of materials and goods.

Taking Control Over Your Driverless Vehicle Fleet

In addition to the general principle of sourcing production equipment from more than one supplier, the fact that different manufacturers to some extent have specialized in different machine types means that most warehouses and factories have AGVs and AMRs from more than one provider.

It is not uncommon for an end user to have two types of automated forklift trucks from one provider, AMRs moving small goods from another, and perhaps a purpose-built mobile robot from a third. Many AGV and AMR providers have developed their own solutions for localization, guiding, and traffic control. For an end user with driverless vehicles from more than one provider, it means that the staff needs to learn how to operate and maintain different system types that are not adapted to each other. The platforms also differ when it comes to user interfaces and terminology, but the real problem is that the risk of traffic jams and deadlocks increase when the systems are not integrated. And for AMRs, which are supposed to function autonomously, the difficulties increase significantly when more than one is deployed in a common workspace.

All this, in turn, has a negative impact on the throughput of goods, which leads to a longer ROI than initially expected. Therefore, the demand for interoperability among different technologies and cooperation among vendors is increasing, according to *The Robot Report*. And although the Robotics Industries Association (RIA) and other bodies are working on standards, there is still a long way to go before AGVs and AMRs from different providers can operate seamlessly together.

Therefore, a common system for navigation and traffic control has many advantages: It provides a unified process integration with other systems such as conveyors, palletizers, and warehouse management systems, a unified training platform, a user-friendly fleet management interface, and, as a result, a smooth and predictable materials flow.

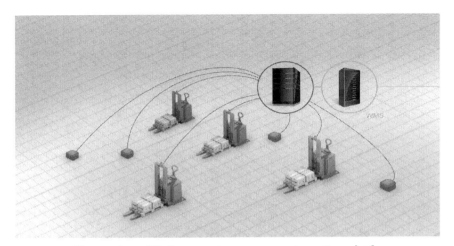
Illustration of Kollmorgen's common automation platform

Take-Home Message
With a common platform for the entire fleet you get:
- Easy process integration   -Optimized traffic/fleet management
- One user interface   - Fast learning
- Seamless scaling

Using a common automation platform for all AMRs and AGVs, such as NDC Solutions from Kollmorgen, saves time and money and enables the end users to focus on their core business activity. It is a generic, complete, and scalable platform that we have developed with the kind assistance of our worldwide partner network. It suits all types of AGVs, AMRs, and mobile robots from small and simple to big and complex.

Peter Bladh is the Director of Product Management and Marketing at Kollmorgen. He has had multiple roles within software development, IT, and product management. He holds an Executive MBA degree from the School of Business, Economics and Law at the University of Gothenburg.

EVOLVING PAST ROBOTIC AMBITION TO ADOPTION

Tom O'Donnell

- Yale Material Handling Corporation -

Warehouse robotics are past the awareness stage. From mobile robots to robotic piece-picking systems, these increasingly capable robotic solutions have become regular fixtures at warehousing and automation events and in trade and business publications across the globe.

Instead of building an understanding of robotic capabilities and theoretical value, distribution center managers are asking for practical guidance to turn robotic ambition into adoption.

To set operations up for a successful robotics investment, there's plenty to consider. The pace of change keeps accelerating — what does that mean for today's robotic technologies? Will they become outdated in a couple years like the newest smartphone? And that's just the tip of the iceberg — questions abound regarding employee acceptance, IT, integration, long-term planning, and more.

Appoint an Internal Champion

Whether tapping an existing resource or hiring a specialist, more companies are assigning an internal champion to be responsible for automation throughout the organization. This resource is in charge of finding answers to the aforementioned questions, coordinating automation projects, and more.

They act as a bridge between outside experts and the unique demands of their operation, identifying best-fit applications for robotics and managing return on investment. Implementation is an especially critical time for an internal champion. With a consistent point of contact, technology suppliers get the access and resources they need for efficient implementation and commissioning, including everything from sufficient Wi-Fi bandwidth to IT configuration for integration with WMS or other enterprise software systems.

Internally, they're responsible for creating a culture of acceptance. They must educate internal staff on how robotics will be used and benefits for both the operation as a whole and each individual employee.

Turnover in this position can delay or even derail a robotics installation. Communication slows, timelines get pushed, and a level of legacy knowledge leaves the process, forcing new internal contacts and automation suppliers to play catch-up.

Understand Available Technologies

Part of understanding what robotics can do and how they fit in the short and near term is a basic understanding of technology. Mobile robotic solutions commonly use LiDAR, a laser-based navigation technology that produces a two-dimensional view of the facility by looking for hard features like columns, walls, and racking. Like any technology, navigation for mobile robotics continues to evolve. At present, some LiDAR systems have a range of 60 feet, but in the future, this will extend to 90 feet, then eventually an evolution from 2D to a full 360-degree, 3D view — looking at the ceiling, in addition to walls and racks.

What does this evolution mean for operations using or considering a solution with a contemporary LiDAR system? Rest easy. Rather than a slow degradation over time like many consumer-oriented tech products, current-gen mobile robotic technology will continue to perform as designed.

Qualify Your Operation's Workflows

With an internal champion leading the charge and technology understood, it's time to figure out where robotics fit in daily operations. Today's robotic solutions are designed with a certain set of tasks in mind. Managers must identify the best-fit workflows to deploy robots, in which their capabilities can be leveraged for maximum effect.

Are there turnover-prone positions that are a struggle to adequately staff? Better yet, are these positions characterized by repetition or long horizontal movements?

Using positions with consistent staffing challenges as a guide, find where robotic abilities overlap to automate entire processes or key repetitive elements.

Basic functions like load transportation, storage, and retrieval are particularly well suited for automation. Robotic lift trucks, for example, have the point-to-point navigation capability to provide consistent, round-the-clock transport productivity, and more advanced solutions can even autonomously reach deep into storage racks up to 30 feet high.

Robotics suppliers require a common set of facility-specific information to qualify an operation for robotics and then design and quote a solution. This includes:

- Facility CAD drawing, preferably with stops and aisles highlighted
- Load dimensions and weight range
- Throughput levels
- Aisle widths
- Travel distance
- Speed limit
- Future goals

Plan for phased implementation

Just as Rome was not built in a day, transitioning to automation does not happen overnight. A longer process done right will always be more effective than an error-filled rush to the finish.

Operations should consider a phased approach to robotics, moving incrementally from simpler to more complex tasks across various applications and workflows. Scaling up in this manner allows the rest of the organization to get comfortable with automation and provides the flexibility to work out any kinks in critical processes.

Planning across five to ten years can account for the continued evolution of technology and a changing competitive landscape. A longer-term master plan also provides a critical platform to share future developments and gain buy-in for continued capital investment.

The Knowledge to Get Up and Running

According to the *2019 MHI Annual Industry Report*, 87% of survey respondents identified robotics and automation as technologies that will have a significant impact on the supply chain in the next 10 years. With the market showing a greater appetite for robotics, more providers will join the market, and end users must become better-informed consumers of robotics solutions and services. This practical knowledge is critical to select vendor partners, set realistic goals, and ultimately experience successful results. ~

Tom O'Donnell helps manufacturers, warehouses, and other logistics facilities understand where mobile robotics can fit in their operations.

MEET THE NEXT GENERATION OF MOBILE ROBOTS

Jeff Burnstein and Robert Huschka

- The Association for Advancing Automation -

Already a warehouse workhorse, autonomous mobile robots are taking on new work in some challenging environments.

Autonomous mobile robots are already a mainstay in the e-commerce warehouse. They zip around vast stacks of products, ferrying the latest purchases to awaiting parcels for shipment across the world. Mobile robots have been replacing forklifts, pulling 1,000-kg payloads around a factory. Robots are stitching together production processes by moving products from one conveyer belt to another. They'll even clean the floors.

Today, autonomous mobile robots (AMRs) are changing the landscape across many environments – from factories to grocery stores to farms. Businesses are drawn to the increasing flexibility and diversifying of their applications.

And the easy programming and implementation of mobile robots make them attractive to end users. Also, the tight job market is pushing companies to look to automation to solve for worker shortages.

Companies including MiR, Fetch Robotics, Vecna, Locus, Omron, Otto, and others have been continually expanding the capabilities and the potential use cases for autonomous mobile robots. Interest in the technology has been off the charts.

The sale of professional service robots — which includes AMRs — grew 32% in 2018. Logistics systems made up 41% of those sales. In 2019, the Association for Advancing Automation sold out our first-ever Autonomous Mobile Robot Conference — with more than 400 attendees — in Louisville.

We are planning two more AMR conferences in 2020 — the first of which will be in Boston on June 9.

Autonomous mobile robots are known for their unique ability to navigate in an uncontrolled environment with a higher level of understanding via sensors, blueprints, artificial intelligence, 3D or 2D vision, and more. AMRs are highly innovative compared to a traditional automatic guided vehicle (AGV), which is also mobile but uses wires or magnets to navigate a narrowly defined area.

In 2020, we expect the evolution of mobile robots will pick up at even greater speed. Here are a few trends to look for this year:

Mobile Manipulation

Merging a mobile robot with a collaborative robot isn't as easy as it sounds. Multiple companies are working on robotic solutions that harness the mobility of an AMR with the reach and precision of a collaborative arm. These robots could be used to restock grocery store shelves, select products for e-commerce shipments, or even unload tractor-trailers filled with boxes.

One example: Pittsburgh-based IAM Robotics' Swift robot can move around a traditional warehouse and pick individual products of various shapes and sizes off the shelves.

On a much larger scale, Honeywell Intelligrated's mobile robotic unloader uses a giant arm with multiple section grippers to dive into the back of a trailer. Using machine vision and artificial intelligence, the robot identifies the optimal approach to gently extract packages, saving workers from the grueling task.

The benefits of mobile manipulation are clear. Mobile robots are allowing companies to move beyond fixed automation. An arm attached to a robot on the floor can only reach so far. But when a company attaches an arm to a mobile robot, it extends the reach of an entire system, creating new, flexible workflows.

Helping Out in Grocery Stores — and Hospitals

While many AMRs are in factories or warehouses, away from public view, a new breed of robots is rolling along right beside the general public. You can spot them in grocery stores and hotels — even hospitals.

Last year, Walmart announced that it's putting Bossa Nova robots in 350 of its stores. The robots will scan shelves for inventory and check to see that the items are correctly priced. They also note if products are located in the wrong spot. The retail giant, with the help of Bran Corp., is also rolling out aisle-cleaning robots. Other robots are used to detect spills or trip hazards in stores.

Medical applications is another area of growth. Aethon, for example, has unveiled the TUG autonomous robot that can roll through a hospital and securely deliver medicines and clinical supplies. It can also deliver meals from the kitchen to patient floors and return dirty trays.

The Great Outdoors
Traditional robots can have some difficulties when facing off with Mother Nature. Outdoor robots will have to deal with hot and cold temperatures and humid conditions while navigating more complex environments.

Already, AMRs are being tested (by FedEx, Amazon, and others) to solve "last-mile" delivery challenges. Starship Technologies, Kiwi, and others have begun testing small robots that roll along sidewalks on a college campus to deliver food purchases to students. These robots can navigate around people and even understand stoplights.

Farming operations are looking to robots to inspect crops, seed fields, and battle weeds and other pests. Robot makers are working on picking and harvesting applications.

For example, U.K.-based Fieldwork Robots has created a robot and says it will be able to pick 25,000 raspberries a day — 10,000 more than the typical human worker.

The Role of Safety and Standardization

In addition to evolving technology, safety and standardization must play a role in the AMR landscape.

Mobility is a fundamental shift in robotics: a robot that is no longer caged off from its environment. More than 30 years ago, the R15.06 American National Standard for Industrial Robot Safety Standard addressed hazards in an industrial environment where the robot was bolted in place with fencing around the hazard zone. Years later the emergence of collaborative robots removed that barrier as the robot worked in tandem with a person, requiring all new safety measures. Today, autonomous mobile robots are adding another layer of complexity to safety considerations.

In 2020, the Robotic Industries Association, one of A3's daughter associations, is expected to introduce the R15.08 American National Standard for Industrial Mobile Robots and Robot Systems — Safety Requirements. The new standard will address all aspects related to the safety of people around industrial AMRs for manufacturers, integrators, and end users.

The standard describes basic hazards associated with AMRs in an industrial environment and provides requirements to eliminate — or adequately reduce — the risks associated with these hazards.

Our Director of Standards Development, Carole Franklin, is helping coordinate these efforts with dozens of industry experts who volunteer their time to the effort. Franklin notes that the goal of the standard is not to prescribe a specific technological solution but rather state the desired outcome and leave the "how" up to the designers.

In addition to safety standards, users of mobile robots have begun discussing the issues of fleet management and interoperability. At the recent AMR Conference, FedEx's Senior Technical Advisor Aaron Prather said his company and others are beginning to ask these questions.

"How will end users manage multi-AMR environments? How will MiR, Vecna, Locus, and OTTO talk with one another?" asked FedEx's Prather. "A recent audit of ground-support equipment at our Memphis hub found 32 different manufacturers. We use a real-time location system to track all the (robots) inside our four walls."

In 2020, the Association of Advancing Automation will be working with a retail trade association and other groups to explore potential protocols and standards for mobile robot navigation and communication.

The Power of the Data

Beyond just transporting materials from point A to B, the most valuable AMRs will have a data-driven strategy incorporated into them.

Old-school AGVs had little understanding of current inventory or path optimization. But today's AMRs are creating a digital understanding of end-to-end movement. According to recent studies by the IDC research firm, a middle layer of data is now emerging between the operation floor and the overarching business systems. This allows an entire organization to create views deep into data and understand the movement pattern of materials, how to improve, and how to reconfigure processes to get the best results.

Data from IDC's 2018 Commercial Service Robotics Survey shows there is no slowing down of this technology. More than 90% of companies surveyed indicated some plans for commercial service robots in their organizations. The industries with the most active robot deployment are retail and wholesale/distribution. More than 70% of users noted double-digit KPI improvements from increased capacity, productivity, efficiency, operational speed, customer service, inventory turnover, and reduced operating costs.

With an ROI like that, don't expect the rollout of mobile robots to slow anytime soon. ~

Jeff Burnstein is the President of the Association for Advancing Automation (A3), an umbrella trade group representing more than 1,200 global companies focused on robotics, machine vision, motors, motion control, and advanced manufacturing technologies. **Robert Huschka** is A3's Director of Education Strategies. For the latest details about A3 activities, visit www.a3automate.org.

ENVISIONING THE WAREHOUSE OF THE FUTURE

Michael Field

- CEO of The Raymond Corporation-

The dramatic shift in how people purchase and receive goods through e-commerce has shaken the long-standing foundation and business model of warehousing and distribution. By 2021, it's expected that more than 2.14 billion people worldwide will buy goods and services online. The geometric growth of e-commerce has had some interesting initial effects and will prove an engine for change in the future.

Brick-and-mortar stores are competing in a market where large e-commerce merchants can provide shipping in two hours or less with tenfold the item selection. Every crucial logistics stage, from when the product is ordered, processed, and leaves its sender, up until the moment the product reaches its final destination is being reshaped.

Last-mile logistics is quickly evolving into on-demand delivery, oftentimes prioritizing the customer's delivery expectations over what's most cost-efficient for the shipper. Customer experience now determines the trade-offs between selection, cost, and time to deliver. From grocery to retail, curbside pickup for customers accommodates their hectic schedules. Customers simply place their orders online and pick up curbside at their convenience.

These unprecedented challenges and continuous demands have left warehouses and distribution centers seeking solutions. However, between revolutionary technology and the next era of human labor, warehouses will have the customized solutions to provide satisfying customer experiences and game-changing delivery strategies.

Shared Autonomy
There's a misconception that robots will replace human labor. We, however, see a different future in front of us. Shared autonomy and operator-assist technologies will help develop the next era for human labor, make new jobs possible and enable future skillsets.

For more complex or variable tasks, the idea of shared autonomy acknowledges that robots can theoretically operate approximately 60% of the time with success, and human action will still be needed for the remaining 40%, when anomalies occur, like an unexpected pallet condition in warehouse racking or obstruction. With shared autonomy, a human monitoring half a dozen autonomous forklift trucks could remotely see the problem and quickly remedy the obstructed forklift.

Shared autonomy will play an integral role in the 21st century warehouse — reducing human fatigue, improving warehouse throughput, and focusing on value-added processes, such as order picking.

5G for Warehouse 5.0

5G technology will work with shared autonomy and further enable us to adapt. When most people think of 5G, they imagine the possibilities it'll bring for cellular network technology. It will allow for a speed, capacity, and cost aligned with what's needed to successfully transfer significant amounts of data from machine to machine using IoT 4.0 principles.

5G is an enabling technology that will revolutionize the way we're able to live and work. It'll provide customers with a more interactive virtual shopping experience through the addition of a real-time video feed via cellular. Shared autonomy will allow you to give real-time feedback to the person picking out your fruit and vegetables; that way you know exactly what you will be receiving and address any issues with the delivery person all via real-time video.

5G is built on the concept of creating a system that can evolve and adapt to various requirements and new market opportunities throughout its lifetime. It will allow us to optimize and evolve with the latest technology as it's tweaked and perfected. Real-time data will empower us to further optimize the throughput of the warehouse, enable the workforce to be more productive and push innovation across all aspects of the warehouse — inevitably leading into the future Warehouse 5.0 cyber-physical shift beyond IoT 4.0.

21st Century Learning

Revolutionary technology and intralogistics solutions will continue to work hand in hand with the workforce of the future to meet customer demands. "Intralogistics solutions" is not just a buzzword — it's the innovative technology that will advance warehouses deeper into the 21st century.

To create this connection, organizations will seek innovative e-learning training tools that resonate with the new workforce. Training will include interactive and multimedia-based programs, such as virtual reality (VR), augmented reality (AR), and artificial intelligence (AI). VR is an educational solution that not only meets millennials and even Generation Z on familiar technological terms, but it also enables all employees to efficiently learn new concepts.

In addition to continuous learning and education, optimizing facilities and technologies will take warehouse productivity deeper into the 21st century. Converting from a manual to semi-autonomous to fully automated warehouse requires many complex steps. AR will help bridge this gap with visualization for troubleshooting and aid for complex tasks. AI will help accelerate the process to reach these milestones; however, it will not replace human intelligence.

Optimization Before Automation

You simply can't optimize what you haven't standardized and don't measure. Warehouse solutions providers, such as Raymond, are able to audit current systems, analyze data, and identify areas of improvement.

The data used to optimize can provide valuable insights into what works in your warehouse and what doesn't, while creating more space for product and improving workforce productivity and overall efficiency.

As trends require warehouses to compile deeper databases, it's essential we leverage this data to make faster, more informed business decisions. In the past, data was difficult to compartmentalize. With today's technologies, we can connect these various sources of data into valuable insights to form overall warehouse direction and guidance.

Although automated systems are highly independent, they're only as efficient as the other facility processes, they interact with. Automation is not a substitute for defining and optimizing a process. Without Lean Management continuous improvement tools, warehouses only create unnecessary waste when applying automation to existing inefficient processes. Once these measurement tools are in place, you can choose the right level of automation solutions to further enhance that process.

Optimization through continuous improvement will not be a revolution; it will be an evolution. Lean Management approaches, which at times can be an artificial intelligence-based solution, analyze warehouse data and identify areas for stepwise improvement.

These methods will allow warehouses to collect holistic data so as to identify the best process improvement, semi-automated, or automated solutions.

Material handling organizations, including The Raymond Corporation, are creating technology that will develop the next generation's talents to run better and empower people to manage these 5G cybersystems smarter. We expect individuals will be needed as the vital link between what technology makes possible and the marketplace's increasing demands for speed. As we look to the future and anticipate the inevitable increase of online shoppers — whether it be 3 billion, 4 billion, or 5 billion — warehouse solutions providers will act to create an adaptive mentality in warehousing and distribution of goods that permits it to grow with the customer and the future of e-commerce. Don't be surprised if you hear iWAREHOUSE® 5.0 in conversation with at least one Intralogistics Solutions partner. ~

Michael Field is the President and CEO of The Raymond Corporation, a leading material handling, intralogistics, and end-to-end solutions provider.

Illustration of The Raymond Corporation's iWarehouse® platform

THE RACE TO PROOF OF CONCEPT

Kaleb Steinhauer

- CEO of Genesis Dimensions -

The construction industry is one the biggest and most rapidly changing industries in the world. According to Market Watch, the global construction industry was valued at over $17 trillion in 2017, and it is expected to rise to around $24 trillion in 2021.[1] Traditionally, the construction industry is very conservative and prefers not to buy into ideas but rather into complete solutions.

Newer technologies are slowly coming into play and rapidly affecting how the industry works. Leaders in the space are no longer questioning the need for robotics and automation. Now, they are trying to understand what the best way would be to implement new technologies in the construction industry.

Some new technologies may have massive disruptive impacts in the future, while other others may become an afterthought.

Robotics and automation will be key for pushing the construction industry forward. Silicon Valley and other investment areas are beginning to take notice, and the increase in investment will grow over the coming years. Venture capital firms have seen the potential in construction hardware, and they are putting their money where their mouths are. Investment in U.S.-based construction technology companies grew by 324% from 2017 to 2018, and it looks to grow even further in the years ahead.[2] In tech investing people often talk about the potential for "hockey stick" growth, but in the construction industry it is more like "hockey mountain" growth. This is the largest industry in the world, and money is flowing in. However, it is important to be cautious as the technology side of the industry is relatively new. There will be a lot of companies that don't succeed and end up losing millions of dollars.

The current theme in the technological development side of the construction industry can be summed up as a race to "proving the concept." Most companies are trying to secure funding in an effort prove their solution is the best answer to the problem at hand. The industry is still at the beginning of using newer technologies in mainstream construction. Many of these technologies are very hardware focused, which means they can be expensive to research and develop. Hardware technologies tend to have long lead times and require big chunks of capital. Once these technologies are fully developed and implemented, it will finally help show people where to make the money in the industry. There will be another five or so years of behind-the-scenes work that will be required before any of these solutions will have any sort of broad or major impact.

At Genesis Dimensions, we are working with the Department of Defense on 3D printing technology for the industry. We believe there is immense potential for government use with our technology and are hoping to prove our concept while working in a research lab for the next few years. Government buy-in will be a huge part of technology's increasing prevalence in the construction industry. Working with regulators will help us to prove our technology works, and then we can expand more easily into the private sector. However, I believe that 95% of the use for this technology will be DoD focused for the next few years and overall government use will continue to be a significant portion of the market. The materials component of 3D printing will become more and more important as we push to take this technology to market. It will still take about five to ten years for the average person to see any impact at all from 3D printing in construction and about 15 to 20 years before 3D printing in construction becomes the norm.

The next year will be focused on fully researching and developing new construction technologies that have better, more innovative hardware and software. There is no shortage of companies working in the space but proving their technologies are the best solution to the problems ahead will be critical for their success. The biggest hurdles companies will face are the regulatory environment in the industry and changing people's mindsets. The mindsets are already beginning to change as people in the industry see the potential benefits that technology will bring but working through the regulatory issues may take more time in the years ahead.

The industry is poised for extremely rapid growth and disruption but needs more investment and time to develop completely. The next year will start to show which companies have a product that actually works, and which companies are just riding the hype. ~

ENDNOTES

1. Source: https://www.marketwatch.com/press-release/global-construction -market-trend-2019-major-drives-key-players-and-scope-2019-07-17? mod=mw_quote_news
2. Source: https://techcrunch.com/2019/02/16/investor-momentum-builds-for-construction-tech/

Kaleb Steinhauer is the CEO of Genesis Dimensions. Kaleb's solution combines large-scale 3D printing and robotics to revolutionize the construction industry through lower labor costs and limited environmental impact

Source: Kaleb Steinhauer

THE 4TH INDUSTRIAL REVOLUTION AND THE CIRCULAR ECONOMY

Fred van Beuningen

- Managing Partner of Chrysalix Venture Capital -

The 4th Industrial Revolution (4IR) is about connecting physical and cyber networks to allow real-time information flow and actionable insights. Its core components are the Internet of Things (IoT), big data, and a secure and reliable digital infrastructure. The 4IR is characterized by technological development in artificial intelligence (AI), robotics, advanced and additive manufacturing, autonomous vehicles, big data analytics, nanotechnology, biotechnology, materials, energy storage, and quantum computing. These advances are not only disruptive to many industries but pose economic and social challenges for society.

The primary challenge is resource use. Can these 4IR technologies serve humanity without increasing the burden on Earth's overtaxed environment?

The circular economy may be the answer to this dilemma. It has emerged as an alternative industrial model to the prevailing linear model of production and consumption in which goods are manufactured from raw materials, sold, used, and then discarded or incinerated as waste.

The linear approach has led to a massive overshooting of planetary boundaries. Currently, it would take 1.7 Earths to replenish the resources used by human society and absorb the consequent pollution. We only have one planet, however.

The circular model seeks to improve resource productivity and performance by keeping goods in use longer, reusing products or their components, and restoring more of their valuable materials, energy, and labor.

The circular economy model is both restorative and regenerative by design. It promotes the efficient use of materials along with the reduction and, ultimately, elimination of waste. The 4IR could enable the circular economy, which, in turn, would foster new business models that protect Earth's finite resources.

The innovation community must work to develop 4IR and circular economy in tandem. The opportunities and challenges are well defined. The required building blocks are well understood. And the zero-waste vision is much more achievable than entrepreneurs, financiers, and governments may realize.

Circular Opportunities and Challenges

Emerging businesses modeled on circular economics focus on inputs (renewable fuels, biological materials, and recyclable components), waste as a value (recycling and upcycling), life cycle improvement (repair, second life, remarketing), platforms (sharing aimed at asset productivity), and product as a service. The question is, how much economy is there in the circular model, and how can we work from macro to micro?

The good news is that some investors and entrepreneurs have taken notice. Innovation oriented towards the UN's Sustainable Development Goals increasing appeals to a new wave of passionate innovators and financiers who are becoming aware of circular principles.

More good news: 4IR technologies have already enabled these new business models and have attracted support from international bodies. The World Economic Forum (WEF) and its partners in the Platform for Accelerating the Circular Economy (PACE) have identified enabling conditions for the circular economy to take off.

Most important are standards and regulations in materials and processes to allow solutions to scale, change drivers such as taxation and societal engagement, and investment in infrastructure and technology.

Data-enabled infrastructure that is interoperable but tailored to local context will also be essential.

The PACE report also identifies the challenges to scaling circular business models. These include opaque value chains, where the material transparency essential to capture value from multiple life cycles and embedded resources is lacking. In addition, linear product designs and business models currently provide too little incentive for a change and lead to linear lock-in. Other challenges are inefficient collection and reversed logistics that lead to dumping or burning of waste as well as inefficient sorting and preprocessing infrastructures that lack economies of scale.

So, where do 4IR and the circular economy meet?

Building Blocks of The Circular Economy

Let's start with the obvious area of bringing more transparency to material flows. Transparency requires linking up the digital data flow with the physical material flow. The resulting data flow must capture the product life cycle journey, which includes the provenance of materials and components, how these were assembled into a product, and product condition and ownership during use.

How would we do this?

A digital product passport could travel with the product throughout the chain. This passport could be stored on a device itself, in the cloud, or on a blockchain solution. It would be accessed by scanning a unique cryptographic anchor to authenticate the product and establish a link between the product and the data flow.

The anchor can be physical like a watermark, digital like a RFID tag, or biological like a DNA marker. For visibility on all materials, the product passport data should feed into an **Internet of Materials (IoM),** a decentralized system connecting data on products and materials through a standardized communication protocol. Data confidentiality and anonymity are key to avoiding competitive challenges.

Companies are already developing the foundation for an IoM. For instance, Dutch startup Circularize develops a blockchain-based communication protocol to promote value chain transparency without public disclosure of the datasets of value chain partners. Decentralized solutions for food production are also developing IoMs.

Direct trade and fair trade promote sustainable sourcing of products like cotton and coffee beans. This helps to save important resources such as water and provide detailed insight into the value chain behind certified products. Similarly, London-based Everledger promotes transparency in the diamonds supply chain by applying a suite of technologies like blockchain, machine learning, and IoT.

Today, inefficient sorting and reversed logistics of waste are being addressed by innovative companies like AMP robotics, which use an intelligent robotics platform to improve the sorting of very heterogeneous waste streams.

They've shown that sensor technology, robotics, and AI are key to developing applications that will revolutionize waste sorting.

AI also enables and accelerates the transition to a circular economy. Three key aspects of a circular economy demand AI solutions: designing circular products, components, and materials; operating circular business models; and optimizing infrastructure to ensure circular flows of products and materials. For example, AI for dynamic pricing is used by Stuffstr to achieve good margins between the sellers of used goods and the second-hand market. Optoro uses AI and predictive analytics to help retailers and brands manage, process, and sell returns and excess inventory through the highest-value channel.

The No-Waste Vision

The big question of the circular economy is how to realize the "no-waste" vision. Municipal solid waste (MSW), the collected waste of municipalities, is a handful: 2 billion tons annually. One option, exemplified by companies like Enerkem in Canada, is to efficiently gasify waste into energy.

Food waste, however, the largest MSW component, now largely goes to waste. New biological technologies to convert food waste into higher-value products than compost include aerobic digestion for fertilizer and feed, fermentation for polymers, mealworms and black soldier fly (BSF) larvae for feed and fertilizer, and (thermo)mechanical conversion to fibers.

Plastic waste, while representing only a small percentage of MSW, has arguably received the most interest with respect to the circular economy. Plastic waste is more prevalent in the environment due to its lack of biodegradability.

But new plastic-recycling technologies show immense promise. These include pyrolysis to convert mixed plastic waste to a synthetic crude oil, chemical recycling to convert plastic (primarily PET) to monomers, and solvent recycling to physically separate plastic from multi-material packaging.

Biological plastic recycling may offer a compelling alternative for scenarios that lack economic incentives or require high energy use. For instance, microbes can be used to selectively replace chemical compounds in products that are hydrocarbon based today.

Mimicking Nature

In nature, there is no waste. One organism's waste is another's nutrients, so energy and materials circulate without creating pollution. The Circular Economy is modeled on this elegant system. It is biomimicry that applies principles of industrial ecology to society at a systems level. Its goal should be to restore the earth's natural carbon, hydro, and heat cycles to sustainable functionality. The circular economy, a merging of technological and natural synergies, is a transformational agenda. When 4IR companies integrate circular principles into their products and culture, the results can be impressive.

The Circulars, an award program hosted by the WEF, Forum of Young Global Leaders, and Accenture Strategy, show just how far circular innovation has come. A 2019 winner, Winnow, maker of a commercial kitchen smart meter, has helped thousands of kitchens cut food waste in half.

Lehigh technologies, another Circulars winner, has turned end-of-life tires into micronized rubber powder (MRP), which replaces oil-based feedstocks. They've created 500 million new tires using this new circular model.

Moreover, banks like Rabo, ABN-AMRO, and ING have introduced financial models for the circular economy, while governmental bodies, including the European Commission, have developed frameworks to overcome market and cultural barriers to the circular economy. These are all encouraging signs.

In the hands of responsible and passionate entrepreneurs, the suite of 4IR technologies, from next-gen robots and IoT to biotech and additive manufacturing, can unlock the power of the circular economy and restore nature's cycles. Once the circular economy is set in motion, it will develop a momentum of its own.

As a wise man once said, "We make our tools, and then our tools make us." ~

ENDNOTES

1. Source: https://www.optoro.com/?ref=Welcome.AI
2. Source: https://www.mckinsey.com/Business-Functions/Sustainability/Our-Insights/Artificial-intelligence-and-the-circular-economy-AI-as-a-tool-to-accelerate-the-transition
3. Source: http://www3.weforum.org/docs/WEF_Harnessing_4IR_Circular_Economy_report_2018.pdf
4. Source: https://www.circularise.com/about
5. Source: https://www.amprobotics.com/technology-overview
6. Source: https://www.choxplore.nl
7. Source: http://sustainability.c-and-a.com/sustainable-products/sustainable-materials/more-sustainable-cotton/organic-cotton/
8. Source: https://www.chainvu.com/blockchain-food-supply-chain

9. Source: https://www.climate-kic.org/innovation-spotlight/ai-and-robotics-could-revolutionise-municipal-waste-sorting/
10. Source: https://www.stuffstr.com
11. Source: https://thecirculars.org/our-finalists
12. Source: https://www.triboo.nl/blog/triboo-joins-circular-coalition-and-signs-partnership-at-dutch-design-week-2019
13. Source: https://www.rabobank.com/en/press/search/2018/20180702-abn-amro-ing-and-rabobank-launch-finance-guidelines-for-circular-economy.html
14. Source: https://www.paconsulting.com/insights/2018/sustainability/united-nations-global-compact/
15. Source: https://biomimicry.org

Fred van Beuningen is Managing Partner at Chrysalix Venture Capital. Fred's industry expertise spans C-level, Executive Board and CEO positions in oil & gas, chemicals, logistics, innovation and sustainability, and scaling-up ventures; he is based in the Netherlands.

THE ROLE OF ROBOTICS IN THE E-COMMERCE ERA

Robert Handfield

- Professor at NC State University and Author -

I recently had the opportunity to hear Janet Yellen, the former Fed Chair, on her thoughts relative to the current economic picture, at the ISM meeting in April 2019. Ms. Yellen's comments reflected many of the observations we've discovered through our workshops this semester on labor challenges in the logistics sector, as well as the incredible growth of the economy.[1]

"Labor force participation is flat, and the participation rates are going up. They plummeted during the great recession during the financial crisis, with a weak economy. Many people searched actively enough, many became discouraged, and didn't search actively enough.

"As the labor market strengthened, they have come back into the labor force. But prime age labor force participation has risen over and above that fact.

"As we try to drive down costs to find low-cost labor in supply chains, the more important issue is technological change, and *ROBOTICS* — which has boosted the demand for skilled labor and led to offshoring and a reduced need for less skilled labor. This has resulted in a loss of jobs that can be offshored, and the downward pressure on wages. Since the late 90s, the real wages have been going down for men, and this seems to most economists that this has nothing to do with the Great Recession. This is a longer-run issue that reflects globalization and social impacts."[2]

In addition, a recent story in *The Wall Street Journal* trumpeted that "the job market doesn't get much better than this. The U.S. economy has added jobs for 100 consecutive months. Unemployment recently touched its lowest level in 49 years (3.7%). Workers are so scarce that, in many parts of the country, low-skill jobs are being handed out to pretty much anyone willing to take them — and high-skilled workers are in even shorter supply."[3]

This is good news for workers, especially those on the low end of the education spectrum, and the growth of new jobs will require in most cases a high school diploma. However, the problem that we are seeing is that organizations cannot find the workers they need to operate their supply chains! The shortage of workers is causing companies to look at non-traditional sources, including individuals with a criminal record. *The Wall Street Journal* notes that if the Federal Reserve continues to keep rates low in the face of low unemployment, this condition could last for a good while.

Will Truck Driver Shortages Lead to Driverless Vehicles? (Unlikely)

The shortage of workers has hit the trucking and logistics industry particularly hard.[4] Freight rates are on the rise, and there are signs that the shortages are unlikely to abate. The federal government is also recognizing this problem and is taking action. Lawmakers in the Senate and House introduced on Feb. 26 legislation to address the urgent shortage of truck drivers.[5] The DRIVE-Safe Act updates federal law to empower the trucking industry to fill these gaps with a qualified, highly trained emerging workforce. It removes age restrictions on interstate transportation by licensed commercial drivers and strengthens safety-training standards across the industry. Young adults become eligible to seek commercial driver's licenses at age 18 in most states; however, federal law currently prohibits these commercially licensed adults from driving across state lines before age 21.

Does this mean that we are going to have driverless trucks soon? Unlikely... although the possibility of "pontooning" trucks is possible. Missy Cummings, a professor at Duke University, notes that "The most likely candidates for automation are in automated rail, but in the US, we are way behind... there are 3rd world countries that have more successful and more advanced automated rail systems. Drones are coming very slowly, with FedEx and UPS moving slowly, but there no technological reasons why they will not evolve. (There are some sociotechnical concerns however)."

But driverless cars!

In her opinion: "We are not ready for it, but that is the power of lobbying markets. And car companies are cutting deals with Uber, Lyft — and there is a big business out there, but it is much too early in the evolution of technology for driverless vehicles."[6]

A number of other comments by executives at a workshop we held on warehouse worker shortages also emphasized how these problems are impacting operations: [7]

- "Our challenge is primarily recruiting millennials and finding modern ways like social media to recruit them...."
- "Since Amazon came in with higher wages, there is pressure from the industry to increase wages now...."
- "Automation can solve labor issues ... but requires multiple-million dollars investments. Maybe driverless trucks are the answer in the long run...."
- "As machine learning and AI is ramping up, it will be important that we look at our automation strategy. To do this, we have to look at our data, which for the most part is in a very antiquated state."
- "As employees near retirement, our ability to get new employees into the business and attract people into this type of work is a real challenge. One facility has low turnover and one has higher turnover — we see a real difference in slower productivity, more shipping errors, and less continuous improvement going on."

The Greatest Potential for Automation is the Warehouse![8]

The implication of all of these signs is clear. Organizations are going to seek automated solutions because they simply cannot operate their supply chains through traditional means. And the biggest opportunity here is the warehouse, for a number of reasons. First, warehouses are becoming a very hot commodity in real estate markets because of the rise of e-commerce. A recent article in Bloomberg suggests that warehouses are now becoming one of the hottest investments in the market, based on recent moves by the Blackstone Group LP, who are betting $18.7 billion on the shift towards e-commerce.[9] This is a perfect example of how the physics of supply chains, which are often overlooked, are fundamental to understanding and enabling the "digital transformation" that is discussed so often in the press.

Go back a decade or more, and the warehouse was where inventory stayed until needed. It was seen as a cost rather than a tool for competitive advantage. As such, the primary focus was on maximizing space utilization.

The rise of Amazon and other e-commerce companies has increased the need for warehouse space by retailers seeking to expand their digital operations and cut delivery times.[10] The shift toward online shopping is reconfiguring supply chains and shaping the fortunes of industrial landlords, with demand especially high in and around large cities, where e-commerce has taken off fastest. Online shopping in the United States is climbing. Retail e-commerce sales for the first quarter totaled $137.7 billion, an increase of 3.6% from the last three months of 2018, U.S. Department of Commerce data released in May.

Total retail sales, meanwhile, were estimated at $1.34 trillion, virtually unchanged.[11]

As a result of e-commerce, things are more complicated today. Internet retailing has created next-day delivery expectations, and warehousing has changed to suit. What were finished goods warehouses have become distribution centers (DCs) with far higher levels of picking and packing activity than was previousiy the case. Mixed pallets, individual cases, and totes are more common, and there are more returns to process. Quality, in terms of both accuracy and damage avoidance, is a bigger issue than ever. Yet at the same time, these "high velocity" DCs are still required to drive labor costs to the absolute minimum.

Even in the more traditional raw materials-type warehouse, demands have changed. Customer expectations for customization means more variety, both in parts/materials and in packaging. Shorter lead times mean increased changeover frequency in production, and that translates to more warehouse activity. And as in the DC world, pressure to drive down costs is relentless.

Types of Warehouse Automation

Beginning with hardware automation, there are many automation tools emerging to replace workers. These include Automated Storage and Retrieval Systems, (AS/RS) automated conveyor systems, AGVs, and pallet flow racking systems. For automating the capture and use of inventory records, warehouse operators are turning to Warehouse Execution Systems (WES).

Warehouse AS/RS

These move pallets from receiving areas into storage locations and bring them back out for buffering, sortation, and picking. The actual movement is done by pallet racking systems that may or may not include telescopic fork load extraction devices, while the racking itself is mobile, allowing for high-density, multiple deep storage. The two biggest benefits of an AS/RS are labor savings and improved space utilization. Many operators also report energy savings as warehouses operate lights out (though temperature and humidity requirements may remain.) Note, also, that applying Industry 4.0-type sensor technology can improve uptime while reducing maintenance requirements.

Automated Conveyor Systems

Conveyors move product — typically bags or cases — from one place to another. They can take them out to the loading dock or bring it from dock to AS/RS. Powered conveyors are an efficient means of raising product to higher floors or bringing it down.

Advanced conveyor systems come with "zero pressure" features. This means cases or bags don't press against others stopped at a gate or barrier, which helps prevent damage. Likewise, controlled acceleration and deceleration prevent spills and damage.

Conveyor systems reduce manual handling and the need for fork trucks. Productivity rises and labor costs are reduced, along with injuries and the claims that result. And for manufacturing, automated conveyor systems deliver and remove product without delays, preventing congestion and stoppages.

AGVs

Otherwise known as autonomous guided vehicles, these can be an alternative to conveyor systems in some warehouse environments. AGVs follow a route around a warehouse, retrieving and delivering cases, totes, and pallets as required. Like conveyors, they reduce the need for manual labor but lack speed and capacity for some situations.

Pallet Flow Racking

These use gravity as the energy source for moving pallets into and out of storage locations. Obviously, this limits the use to situations where pallets are moving down rather than up. Pallet flow systems work well in cooler and freezer environments and can be configured for either LIFO or FIFO storage. In common with conveyors, they reduce manual handling and use of fork trucks — but don't yield the same magnitude of benefits as an AS/RS.

Warehouse Execution Systems

A WES integrates a warehouse management system with warehouse control for superior visibility into material movement and storage. It improves space utilization while reducing transportation effort through optimized location selection. By linking with tracking and identification (barcodes, RFID), warehouse execution systems improve data accuracy and reduce product losses. Perhaps best of all, a WES enables paperless operation, saving time while reducing errors.

For a lean, highly automated manufacturing operation, the benefits of a well-implemented WES are substantial.

Higher data accuracy means fewer errors, translating to fewer production stoppages/changeovers and higher OEE.

Despite these automation tools, there will continue to be a demand for workers with the skills to work with these automated solutions. Don't expect complete automation with robots to occur anytime in the next five years! ~

ENDNOTES

1. Source: https://scm.ncsu.edu/scm-articles/article/workshop-addressing-labor-shortages-in-warehouse-and-dc-operations
2. Source: https://scm.ncsu.edu/scm-articles/article/comments-from-former-fed-chief-janet-yellen-at-ism-meeting-2019
3. Source: https://www.wsj.com/articles/inside-the-hottest-job-market-in-half-a-century-11551436201
4. https://scm.ncsu.edu/scm-articles/article/workshop-addressing-labor-shortages-in-warehouse-and-dc-operations
5. Source: https://www.mhlnews.com/labor-management/congress-introduces-plan-address-truck-driver-shortage
6. Source: https://scm.ncsu.edu/scm-articles/article/missy-cummings-from-duke-on-logistics-automation-were-going-in-reverse
7. Source: https://scm.ncsu.edu/scm-articles/article/workshop-addressing-labor-shortages-in-warehouse-and-dc-operations
8. Source: https://scm.ncsu.edu/scm-articles/article/improving-your-manufacturing-operations-using-warehouse-automation
9. Source: https://www.bloomberg.com/news/articles/2019-06-03/blackstone-buys-18-7-billion-u-s-property-assets-from-glp?utm_campaign=news&utm_medium=bd&utm_source=applenews
10. Source: https://scm.ncsu.edu/scm-articles/article/warehouses-are-the-next-hot-investment-triggered-by-the-digital-transformation-of-the-supply-chain
11. Source: https://www.census.gov/retail/mrts/www/data/pdf/ec_current.pdf

Robert Handfield is the Executive Director of the North Carolina State University's Supply Chain Resource Cooperative. The SCRC is a university-industry partnership dedicated to advancing the supply chain industry and the professionalism of its practitioners.

AGVS AND LI-ION BATTERIES: A MATCH MADE IN HEAVEN

Maxim Khabur

- Marketing Director of OneCharge -

Automation brings unprecedented opportunities for the warehouses to improve operating efficiency and reduce costs. Among other innovations, Automated Guided Vehicles (AGVs) are getting momentum.

An automated guided vehicle (AGV) system is computer-controlled, wheel-based load carrier (normally battery powered) that runs on the plant or warehouse floor (or, if outdoors, on a paved area) without the need for an onboard operator or driver (MHI definition). Essentially, it is a mobile robot.

The Pioneer Companies
To make an AGV, you need a truck, a connected computer with sensors, and motive power. Balyo, a manufacturer of the "brains" for AGVs, partnered with Hyster-Yale Group and Linde.

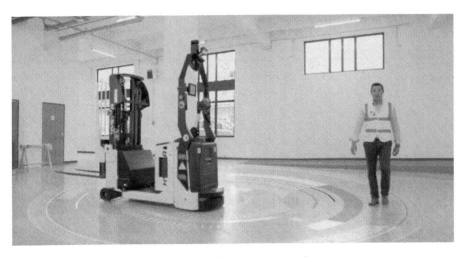
Source: Maxim Khabur — OneCharge

At the start of operations three years ago, Balyo researched available options for motive power for their offering and decided to go with lithium batteries. Baptiste Mauget, Vice President of Marketing at Balyo, said the key requirement was automated charging system, so electric power was an obvious choice: "The best energy solution for robots is lithium batteries. We chose LTO chemistry for its longest cycle life and highest availability." Baptiste further explains that "availability" of AGV in effect means uptime, when the vehicle is not paused for charging.

AGVs are sold by the advanced Material Handling equipment dealers, like PAPÉ. Balyo has supplied a few of its AGVs to PAPÉ's demo facility in Seattle, where warehouse managers can see these robots in action.

Shane Fairbanks, Seattle Facility Manager: "AGVs are mostly applicable in operations involving 'stacker' lift trucks, where you need to pick things from a conveyor and stack them on shelves.

Automotive, pharmaceutical or logistics business are good examples." Shane said that customers value AGVs because they can run 24/7 without needing an operator. With tangible efficiency improvements, AGVs are starting to get traction with technologically advanced companies with high volumes of material handling and warehouse space. You guessed it right — Amazon. "AGVs in our offer are 100% electric, and all of them run on Li-ion," Shane noted.

OneCharge manufactures Li-ion batteries for the material handling industry, with over 450 of models for Class I, II, and III lift trucks, sweepers, scrubbers, and ground support equipment at airports.

Source: Maxim Khabur — OneCharge

OneCharge has supplied Li-ion batteries to PAPÉ's demo AGV trucks in April 2018, and Shane says that clients' interests in AGV solutions have started to pick up in the last few months. He calls it the "Amazon effect on things." "Bigger companies may be slow on the adoption, but they have the money to experiment, and once they test and prove a solution, others follow in a stream," Shane says.

Why Lithium-Ion?

Facilities that use AGV lead-acid battery-powered fleets consistently face about 20% asset downtime. This is due to the five to six hours of battery charging required for each AGV each day. Additionally, each lead-acid battery is required to be down for another eight hours weekly for trickle charging and cell equalization.

Indeed, Li-ion batteries' benefits are even more pronounced with AGVs: Significantly less charging time overall and flexible charging schedule, zero daily maintenance, and stable voltage with higher travel and lifting speeds provide minimum downtime and the highest operational efficiency. In the case of OneCharge batteries, one can expect enhanced safety and advanced data capabilities with the top-notch battery management system, and one can't fail to recognize that AGVs and Li-ion is a perfect match!

Spirit AeroSystems is one of the world's leading designers and manufacturers of aerostructures, which provides products and solutions for both commercial and defense customers, including Airbus and Boeing.

In late 2018 Spirit AeroSystems has started a demo project to stress-test one AGV Li-ion battery, which was recommended to them by Green Energy Concept Inc., consultant and installer of motive power solutions. After nine months the whole fleet of company's lift trucks in Kinston, North Carolina, is switching to OneCharge Li-ion batteries.

Most of Spirit AeroSystems' North Carolina facility lift trucks are AGVs and MGVs (manually guided by an operator with a remote control). The company was permanently facing problems with maintenance and overall reduced run time with the sealed lead-acid / TPPL batteries they were using for the last five years. The main reasons for switching to Li-ion were increased operational demands, which the old lead-acid batteries could not support any longer.

Source: Maxim Khabur — OneCharge

Allen Grady, Equipment Maintenance Manager at Spirit AeroSystems: "We have a large facility to manufacture parts for AirBus A350, and we use lift trucks to move around big tools 24 hours a day. We had to stack spare lead-acid batteries at a special section of our facility and install special ventilation and other safety features there. Each truck was down for at least 30 to 40 minutes six times a day (twice per shift) charging big and heavy batteries. Big hassle and big loss of time! With the new Li-ion technology, we managed to sync our production schedule with batteries charging. It is now only once or twice per day, the battery stays inside the truck, and it takes 1 to 1.5 hours to fully charge a battery."

Oliver Kuarsingh, Director at GECI, said: "OneCharge batteries can stand much more abuse and need much less attention compared to lead-acid batteries. ROI calculations and overall stability of OneCharge Li-ion batteries were the main reasons we recommended OneCharge to Spirit AeroSystems."

Driving Style: Autonomous Vehicles vs. Humans

How is battery performance different when used by human driver compared to Automated system? In their article in *Electronics and Test*, Sudhi Uppuluri and Doug Kolak are discussing the relative performance of an electric car driven by a human and by an autonomous driver. It turns out that humans are much less gentle with the motor and battery. What it actually means is that performance boost for the warehouse with AGVs' introduction can be amplified by even higher battery performance and less downtime for charging and maintenance when a truck is controlled by a computer.

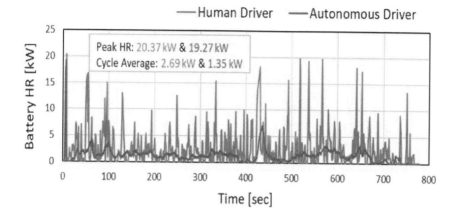

Source: Maxim Khabur — https://www.designnews.com/electronics-test/
how-autonomous-driving-affects-heat-loads-and-component-sizing-electric-
vehicles/41833506461562?
ADTRK=InformaMarkets&elq_mid=10411&elq_cid=4827409

Who Should Pay Attention?

The AGV and Li-ion combination can dramatically improve any warehouse or conveyor operation, with the efficiencies and savings mounting with scale.

We expect the following industries follow the trail blazed by pioneers like Amazon and Spirit AeroSystems: pharmaceuticals, hospital, automotive, aerospace, paper, printing, warehouses & distribution, lumber & furniture, electronics, steel & metal.

Food and beverages processing and distributing should also lead the way for safety reasons (both lead and acid fumes are no toy in the same warehouse with food). In the cooler and freezer environment, the FROST options of Li-ion batteries are indispensable.

Today there are a few types of battery technologies used in AGVs, including: flooded lead acid and TPPL, NiCad, fuel cells. But the experts are unanimous — AGVs and Li-ion batteries is a match made in heaven! ~

Maxim Khabur is the Marketing Director at OneCharge Lithium Batteries. He holds a Master's degree from Hult International Business School.

2020: BOTH UTOPIA AND DYSTOPIA

Russell Nickerson

- Founder of Collabots and Lab Manager of MassRobotics -

The year 2020 will be significant in the robotics industry. In science fiction of yore, 2020 is one of those years that was an easy fictional number to grab from a hat. It is a date that indicated a time far enough ahead that whatever was hypothesized would *hopefully* no longer be relevant. With some luck and/or hitting a cultural nerve, maybe even some of the fiction would turn out to be true. Surely by 2020, we should have all of our problems figured out. Will 2020 bring either utopia or dystopia?

The economic climate is always morphing, giving economists a tough time. In a recession, amazing things can be achieved because roboticists are forced to work with the bare essentials. From a different standpoint, those startups that have found funding or clients are often too valuable to sacrifice and cut away in a downturn.

Of course, some products and projects will be deemed frivolous, but the true live changing automation elements will not only rise but be inundated with talent that had to abandon their less fruitful endeavors. Robotics is nearly recession proof because we always need to work towards the bleeding edge, and robotics will always be there as an alternative to (at least) physical human incapability. Robotics will always take time to mature to market, and it will always be a risk because it involves such a wide variety of talent that a team needs to blend together just right.

Similar to the downturn of retail, I foresee stalwart industry brands not being able to provide lower-cost robots in line with mid-size competitors. It will be an acquisition spree, with larger companies grabbing robotics startups that can slim down their costs with smart solutions and changes in architecture. Trade frictions will spur national growth in production; industrial robots will be the only way to meet demand. There will be some core companies that provide the right product(s) that will rise to be new global leaders.

The race to 5G and overall bandwidth capabilities will bring some amazing new technology. The problematic details are in what major conglomerate will win the race. Will they be fair? Will this perpetuate internet company monopolies or actually open the free market? If general internet becomes cheaper and the fountain overfloweth with bandwidth, expect a huge global economic shift for whatever country enables that first. On the flip side, the powers that be in tech are likely to opt to wring the pockets of everyone with rigid, unappealing packages.

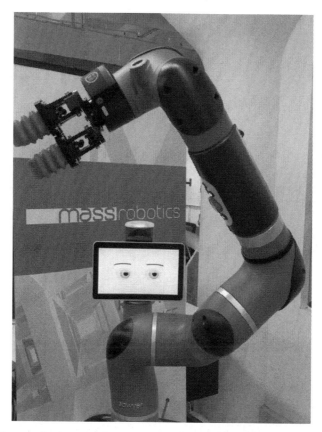

Sawyer looks to pick up items with the Soft Robotics gripper
Source: Russell Nickerson

Stylistically, I anticipate the "cyberpunk" aesthetic made popular by movies such as *Blade Runner, Ghost in the Shell,* and *The Matrix* will rise in popularity. Wearables and fabric innovations will come in lockstep with this scene. Google Glass gave us the vision: What if I can see my phone without it even in my hand? This type of technology will find its way into the workplace more and more. To attract talent, companies will tout new gadgets and software but unfortunately still maintain outdated business etiquette of the past.

NAO robots prepare for a synchronized dance routine.
Source: Russell Nickerson

Every generation of worker wants more and more time, flexibility, and opportunity to grow and learn. The problem is that the climate no longer rewards longevity and tenure but rather the chance of building your résumé for a bigger role somewhere else.

In years before, it was the old tale of climbing the corporate ladder. You can start as a janitor and become the CEO with hard work! For most in the 2020 gig economy, it is more like hopping across rocks on a river. If you slip once, you will be sinking from paycheck to paycheck. You might find a nice big salary rock or, if you are lucky, an entire CEO island late in your career.

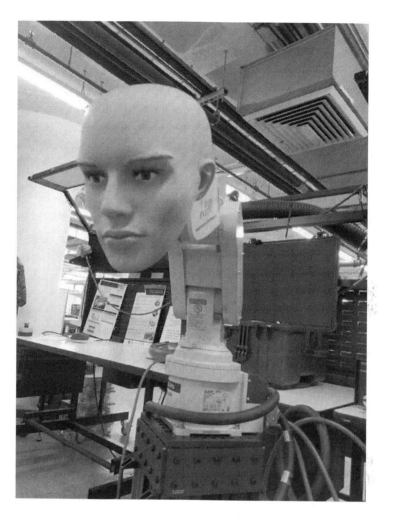

A mannequin head on a Mitsubishi robot arm.
Source: Russell Nickerson

2020 seems like a year that goals will be set, and pieces may not come together but rather be placed on the board. In the coming years more movement might happen, but infrastructure plays are going to be what big businesses want to add to their future. Pipes, roads, transportation, and bridges that are centuries old will need to be refreshed.

With rising costs and taxes that a barely existing middle class can't afford to be raised, where the money comes from to make these infrastructure investments will be hard to find. Innovation and automation primarily in construction will have to be applied to help make renovations happen. The large direct task is creating solutions that can help reduce the physical labor cost and time. The aftermath of what is created is a largely data-driven, near-autonomous maintenance loop that makes sure to replace and repair things before they are too far gone that they are a danger to the public. Long term, infrastructure will be easier to maintain, but the main point of friction will always be "Who is paying for this update?"

The dystopian 2020 will have an influx of security issues. Hackers stealing data, geopolitical issues, privacy issues, and open-source issues will all be in the news often. Automation and artificial intelligence will certainly allow new insights into how humans work. Who controls those insights and how what is learned is implemented into a product is the true issue. From bioweapons to targeted advertisements on media, people are now able to create technology that effects our reality directly.

I anticipate the criticality of urge for action to peak in a *War of the Worlds* scenario where someone uses computer-generated voice and facial-mimicking software to release fictional announcements or incriminating action based on someone (or multiple people) in the government. The news will get a video from a seemingly credible source of the President issuing a direction of war to a country.

The algorithms will get so good that it would be nearly indistinguishable from a real video. How is this media handled?

How can we authenticate it was from a real person? In the example, I used a highly visible figure, but what if someone of lesser stature was framed with a fake video? Currently, the internet is a grey area. People can post anonymously and have multiple accounts, and in general, they have the freedom to post nearly whatever they want. Like any American, I do enjoy my freedom of speech.

However, the silly antics of internet trolls of the past are evolving into strategies to directly affect lives and even the way we think and understand facts. Voices and video are starting to be faked. Imagine your identity stolen not just with credit card numbers but your actual voice and face. Solutions are going to have to be found to verify content for truth, and even those solutions will be under attack.

Utopia and dystopia will coexist in 2020. Expect an influx of tech acquisitions, struggles between infrastructure updates, and their associated rolling fees and security concerns. At least it all should come with neon lights and a thumping synthwave beat. ~

Russell "RoboRuss" Nickerson is the founder of Collabots, where he does robotics consulting, training, and speaking. Russell is also Lab Manager at MassRobotics, a non-profit robotics co-working space located in Boston's Seaport. He has previously worked at Softbank Robotics/Aldebaran on the Pepper and NAO robots.

Robots helping to serve dinner at the Robotics Summit in Boston.
Source: Russell Nickerson

ROBOTICS GROWTH IN THE YEAR AHEAD

Maciej Lisiecki

- Managing Director of Horizon Automation -

It is a well-known fact that the labor pool is a foundation of every factory, warehouse, store, and similar kind of business. Today, every developing country suffers from a lack of a complete workforce. It is obvious that nobody wants to do the simple and boring tasks, nobody wants to lift heavy goods, and nobody wants to operate in unsafe working conditions. Take, for example, millennials or post-millennials: Do you believe they would like to do any from the above? I doubt it.

For the new generations, every aspect of life is automated: Manufacturing, transport, warehousing, everything concerning goods is just nothing more than "click and order" on a smartphone and then "collect" at the door. However, it is not easy to meet those needs. Perhaps the answer would simply be putting robots in all the locations where the goods move and using AI for recognizing customer needs.

Moreover, reacting fast and being close to the buyer would not hurt. And that is what Horizon-Automation actually does, because we understand how automation and robotics support manufacturing and logistics processes.

First of all, I would like to mention a few challenges concerning robotized workstations. The first one is recognizing object with a vision system. Put your sunglasses on, switch the light off, and try to pick up a specified good of a particular color. This is how the vision system sees. It does not see the colors; it is almost blind and generally reacts mainly on light.

The second one is gripping precision. Put your winter gloves on and try to pick up a specified shape from the tote's corner. It is not an easy task; nevertheless, there are some companies that work on gripping mechanics.

The third one is cycle time, performance, and throughput. Grip a 20 lb (10 kg) good and move it fast within the distance of 3ft (1m). These robots have to be closed in cages because current technology isn't able to recognize a collision if heavy things are shifted around quickly. The fourth one is collaborating with people — that is, working with people side by side without hurting them. The fifth one is being adaptive to changing data.

Responding to these five main challenges simultaneously is a tall order, and they almost exclude each other, because how can you move a 20 lb (10kg) good and fast while at the same time keeping a good cycle time and collaborate? Or how can you obtain collaboration, precision, and speed concurrently?

It is almost impossible to cover all the aspects in one application. New sensor technology isn't advanced enough, and due to that fact, we have to choose whether we want to move heavy goods, be precise, be fast, or collaborate with humans.

Taking into consideration the technological requirements and analyzing our research data — that is, how people buy, what drives them, what are the factories and warehouses' needs — we have chosen three ways of robotics and automation technology application.

The first one pertains to collaborative robots that support CNC machines, palletize slowly, and move parts from A to B. It means the cycle time is not critical in this case. Also, the vision system is sometimes supported by machine learning algorithms and recognizes perfectly the shape since it is always the same as well as the position of the good. As a result, the robot can be easily reprogrammed to support another machine or task. What is more, a new gripper or vision system can be installed without much trouble. Nowadays it is quite simple. The market offers several companies manufacturing collaborative robots. Among them, the most popular is Universal Robots, with its supportive webinars and cooperating companies for vision systems, grippers, etc.

Another type of collaborative robot is known as an Autonomous Mobile Robot (AMR). These could be the perfect answer for the transport system, which requires flexibility but not the throughput.

The second kind of application we implement are robots with short cycle time, good recognition/vision system, and good gripping technology. These are the high-end applications supported by machine learning. Machine learning is essential, because it builds on its own the strategy of picking and placing the goods, whereas the static algorithms are not able to do so.

Using the mathematical statistics to modify the decision is critical for lowering the gripping/picking error rate. It directly affects the cycle and throughput of the robot cell. The company KNAPP is a pioneer in this solution and has very high achievements. Watching how the robots use the positive and negative results to learn by themselves is a very pleasant experience. Horizon-Automation is a proud member of the group. They have been already running some applications, but within the next few months, they are going to be installed at new customers' sites.

The third option is a Micro Fulfillment Center or MFC. It is the newest idea invented by Take-Off Technologies, supported by KNAPP with its OSR Shuttle™ Evo and partly implemented in the PLC area by Horizon-Automation. The MFC solution perfectly answers the question of how to sell promise of availability. Why? Because when people buy online, they believe that the goods they see on the screen of a computer or a mobile phone are in store, that they will not be replaced with other ones, that they can be collected or delivered home soon, and that they are available somewhere close to them in one of the well-known supermarkets. It is customer friendly. And what makes Take-Off Technologies' MFC special? It needs a small area; it can be easily fitted in a store or a warehouse.

The robots are the core of this automation; they store the goods on shelves, and they can bring the bins with goods to picking station in a few seconds and according to the orders generated by the host. After that, the AMR robots drive with ready shopping baskets to the buffer. To summarize, in commerce we have at least three very important criteria: time, which requires fast reaction, choice of goods — everything the market offers and the way of delivery. All of them are successfully met by the MFC.

As can be seen, all the three answers cover manufacturing, warehousing, and commerce. What matters most is the fact that the MFC, equipped with collaborative robots, fast picking robots, and AI for analyzing the customer's needs, can fit in all of those areas. It means it is an optimal solution for a manufacturer who needs a small, fully automated warehouse. With time it can be conveniently extended by adding consecutive aisles and more robots.

On the other hand, the MFC can be smoothly connected to an online shop, which is good news for e-commerce runners. It might be, however, a challenge to implement this robotized installation on a larger scale due to ever-present lack of trust for buying online by the brick and mortar shops' customers. ~

Maciej Lisiecki is the Managing Director of Horizon-Automation, a member of KNAPP Group, Fox-Automation LLC, and Izibotic. All these companies have been found as the result of his enthusiasm for robotics & automation. He was born in 1975 in Poland and graduated from the Wroclaw University of Technology.

A GAP IN THE AUTOMATION ENGINEERS MARKET

Łukasz Lipski

- Co-Founder of UnitDoseOne -

In a world where innovation is starting to be the most valuable asset, there are thousands of startups founded every day. Most of them are software based as the entry point is quite low since most of the tools are inside your computer. Hardware startups are more demanding — they utilize wider skillsets and far more tools. Co-founding one showed me the complexity of job descriptions that are fuzzier than in software startups due to unestablished skill categories.

Building the automated drug-dispensing system in UnitDoseOne is complicated enough to begin with. There is a step-by-step process designed by specialists from different areas for taking care of a drug: visually recognizing it, sorting, cutting, packing, storing, and dispensing the drug. This meant we essentially had to create a warehouse in a much smaller space.

To fit into this small space, we had to do two things. First, redesign the process of the automated storage system leaving only the core points. Then, determine the level of engineering our solution would require and find a middle point between reinventing the wheel and using too many off-the-shelf products to keep the machine open for changes. From an automation point of view, it was constant balancing between industrial automation and embedded electronics.

These two worlds were colliding continuously. Reliable servo drives are fairly available, but sadly they are not easy to fit into a concept of modularity as all the excess wiring would require extra space. It would be significantly easier if we could use a separate control cabinet as the whole system would be just another production line.

Trying to find a golden mean, we have managed to stay in between with our own way of wiring industrial systems. In order to achieve that, we developed hundreds of small PCBs containing mostly passive elements for redundancy and managing signals. Making PCBs for our modules let me observe how automation engineers, circuit designers, and embedded systems programmers think. Every one of them had a different point of view with an enormous amount of solutions.

Automation engineers raised questions about EMC of connectors and hardware design. The circuit designer thought about signal interferences and mechanical problems with PCBs. And the embedded systems programmer tried to find a reason for making a whole PCB without any controller.

As enjoyable as it was to oversee this process, it is hard not to notice that it took three people to develop a good design. Although if we had decided to use more high-tech electronics, even these three experts would not be enough.

There would be still have been some qualifications missing.

There is a tendency in the automation market to divide products into two branches: fast implementation solutions and high-tech electronics. The first one is the environment filled with the eye candy products, ready to use with minimal configuration and knowledge needed. Off-the-shelf products with a substantial amount of space required for installation. Even though it is only a generalization of a vast and diverse automation market, we have to remember that it is a business like every other.

The first impression of a product seems to be the most important. Automation engineers and electricians are consumers that can fall for the same tricks as many of us during everyday shopping.

Some companies frequently utilize the second branch and sell their goods as bare PCBs, embedded systems ready for implementation at some level of your design, modules for PLCs, servo drives, motion controllers. It is almost the same product without plastic covers and mounts, yet it requires a deeper knowledge of embedded systems design and electronics to be handled properly.

These two branches are not completely mirrored in employees' qualifications. The first branch is what future automation engineers are formally educated for. It requires handling electrical installations and a mechanical approach for solving everyday problems. Additionally, the ease of use of PLCs and other controllers gives those engineers more time to concentrate on aspects like servo motor parameters, wiring, connectors, and mechanical problems. Nowadays, automation engineers fit right into that branch, although they could solve the same problems with high-tech embedded systems modules on implementable PCBs if it were not for the common knowledge gap.

Embedded systems designers are experienced in coding with a background in electronics, and that gives them a wider skillset in comparison to PC programmers who lack knowledge on hardware design. Both have dependable software tools, but nevertheless the lack of experience in handling physical processes is too significant a factor to be neglected. Automation engineers, on the other hand, with mediocre software support, have an electrical and mechanical knowledge supported with object-oriented coding skills in some cases. However, the experience with embedded systems and PCB design is not present.

Reading that might give the impression that we expect too many skills from one person, but I could not disagree more. In the end, when your design is ready for its implementation and testing, a diagnostician will be needed to debug the whole physical process and oversee electrical installation, PCBs, sensors, software, and hardware.

It does not matter how precise your CAD/software simulation on the computer screen is, the real-life test will include physics and randomness. At least mediocre skills in all the fields above will provide a well-fitted person for this task.

An automation engineer does not have to know how to design PCB. He will only need an outer layer of knowledge to point out a probable defect. His electrical and mechanical background will help to achieve that. Both embedded system developers and PC programmers lack that critical knowledge and important experience.

Unremarked lack of experience with embedded systems can lead to unexpected errors surfacing in late implementation design. That is not the only problem. The common practice of simplifying GUIs in order to achieve ease of use and effective program handling actually reduces programming skills and knowledge.

Yet people are still using that second branch of automation, utilizing skills of embedded systems programmers, electronic circuit designers, or even programmers.

It would be valuable to have the experience and qualifications of somebody standing somewhere between mechanics, electronics, and programmers in order to avoid missing the bigger picture, purpose of the design, and synergy between fields of experience.

Achieving that would require creating a job description clear enough to provide training and education for potential future employees.

I was not aware of this missing link myself. Implementing our solution with small PCBs was truly the great design approach, saving a lot of time and space — and accelerating final launch of the product.

Nevertheless, we did not go deeper into the branch of automation with high-tech embedded electronics. At that time, there were no persons nor qualifications available on the job market. As it turned out, we were looking for a mechatronics engineer, a position described by Tetsuro Mori in 1969. Even though almost 50 years have passed, and technically that job description should be the perfect match for what we were seeking, practically, no formal education could prepare someone for this position. Moreover, a majority of companies emphasize fast implementations with off-the-shelf products, so there is no room to exercise such a skillset.

As a consequence of this state of affairs, mechatronics engineers are almost extinct. Lately, some startups have started to provide a work environment for such engineers. However, due to the high-pressure combination of innovation, time constraints, and mechatronics on those who work as automation engineers, this position will have to emerge as specialization from one of the leading experts such as automation engineers, embedded systems programmers, coders, or PCB designers.

Creating specialists in high-tech electronics with a broad set of skills would enable the aforementioned experts to focus on their matter of expertise and not to overexploit their knowledge in areas they are not specialized for and, in many cases, do not have proper qualifications.

The conclusion is clear: A division in the automation market and aforementioned gap in knowledge are visible in skills offered by few occupational groups. Depending on a manager's abilities to recognize potential and increased possibilities to train employees in missing areas, the design may have completely different outcome. It can be time consuming, resource consuming, or deadly. It is clear that producers are ready to ship their best, but the form is not always manageable for current specialists.

Especially in startups, a more holistic approach for this problem is needed, and the market is trying to rectify it on its own.

With innovation being a priority these days, I would say that the next big thing in automation for 2020 will be the rise of a new specialization having its background in automation but leading in electronic design and programming.

It will open new doors for automation engineers, making them more valuable employees. This new specialisation will bring an ease of implementing industrial-grade solutions in startups and small companies wanting to achieve a high reliability of systems and full scalability of solutions. ~

Łukasz Lipski is the Co-Founder of UnitDoseOne robotic hospital pharmacy as well as CzteryZeroAutomatyka, hosting Pokład MakerSpace initiative for freelancers to bring together knowledge, people, electronics, CNC, FDM, SLA, CAD. Go open source, open hardware! Share your knowledge!

USING AUTOMATION TO MITIGATE SUPPLY CHAIN RISK

Daniel Stanton

- President of SecureMarking -

Executive Summary

With uncertainty high around the world, supply chain technology investments in 2020 should focus on solutions that reduce risk and increase flexibility. From accelerating transaction speeds to decreasing dependence on manual labor, technologies that increase visibility and efficiency throughout the supply chain will help to reduce risk exposure while delivering a return on investment for the business.

Many of these technologies are one-way bridges; they are difficult to implement, but once you adopt them, there is no going back. Early adopters always face uncertainty and may have difficulty justifying the initial cost of these strategic investments. But laggards who cling to legacy solutions can find it even harder to respond to industry changes and risk becoming uncompetitive and obsolete as new technologies transform markets.

Using Automation to Mitigate Supply Chain Risk

2020 promises to be a year of tremendous uncertainty for supply chains. In particular, there are four risk categories that have a high probability of producing supply chain disruptions with profound effects:

- Climate and weather risks. In the United States, we're seeing a growing number of natural disasters with an impact of more than $1 billion.[1]

- Social and political risks. Globally, there is a rise is nationalist policies such as stronger border controls and higher tariffs.[2] There is also a growing concern about the automation of jobs and the impact that it could have on employment, consumption, and policy.[3]

- Economic risks. We have experienced an unusually long 10 years of economic growth. The risk of a recession is increasing each year, and Bloomberg estimates the 2020 recession risk at 25%.[4]

- Technology risks. Technology is a double-edged sword. As new technologies are developed and deployed, they create risks that are often hard to anticipate. For example, technologies may have gaps or bugs, as seen in the grounding of the 737MAX. Or technologies may have vulnerabilities that can be exploited by criminals or adversaries.[5] At the same time, failing to adopt and capitalize on technologies can leave a business vulnerable to competitors.

For those of us in industry, these risks can seem overwhelming. But we'll bear the responsibility to respond to them when they occur. So it makes sense to prepare in advance, because the best defenses against any risk are preparedness and speed. As the old joke goes, you generally don't have to be faster than the bear — you just have to be faster than the person next to you.

It turns out that we can mitigate many of these risks by making strategic investments in technology. There are five strategic investments that appear to be particularly important today. Let's examine each of these areas and illustrate how automation technologies can support our efforts to manage supply chain risks.

Strategy 1: Increase Supply Chain Visibility

The better information you have about what's happening in your supply chains, the more options you have to respond. Visibility has the added benefit of enabling process automation. Some examples of visibility technologies that are becoming more common include Electronic Logging Devices (ELDs) in semitrucks, as well as sensors and Internet of Things (IoT) devices. Visibility solutions rely on communications and storage infrastructure, so the growth of cloud computing and the rollout of 5G wireless capabilities are important enablers, too. Blockchain technologies can also improve visibility by providing a "single source of truth" that can be shared in real time by all of the authorized participants in a supply chain. And supply chain control towers and information aggregators can enable analysis of markets and the ability to quickly identify and respond to disruptions.

Strategy 2: Increase Sources of Supply

There have been a number of attempts at creating digital B2B marketplaces that offer manufacturers, distributors, and retailers a greater selection of suppliers and more competition in pricing. Some of these marketplaces are focused on particular industry verticals (such as Honeywell's GoDirect Trade), some are focused on geographic regions, and some are built around established brands or platforms (such as Amazon Business and eBay Business Supply). There are also opportunities to identify new sources of supply using search engines like Google and social media platforms like LinkedIn.

Strategy 3: Increase Access to Customers and Channels

Digital platforms offer new ways to connect with customers, from marketplaces like Amazon.com to social media networks like Facebook, LinkedIn, and Twitter. Each of these platforms has developed an ecosystem around it, so in order to leverage them successfully, companies need to align with their cultures and capabilities. The upside can be a much stronger, more direct, and more personal connection with individual consumers. For large companies, and those with strong brands such as Nike and Walmart, it may make sense to invest in developing proprietary technologies that allow them to connect with customers without relying on third-party platforms.

Strategy 4: Accelerate Transaction Speeds

There are a growing number of technology solutions focused on increasing the speed of transactions throughout the procure-to-pay and order-to-deliver processes.

For example, IBM Sterling Supply Chain's new order management solutions which instantaneously matches each customer order with all of the available items throughout an enterprise supply chain to select the optimal fulfillment choices.[6] And U.S. Bank's freight audit and payment solution, which automatically matches invoices to freight contracts, eliminating a labor intensive and error-prone manual approval process and accelerating payments to carriers. The faster transaction speeds that these technologies provide become especially valuable by allowing a business to respond quickly when markets are constrained or dynamic.

Strategy 5: Increase Trust Between Parties

There is a growing threat of fraud in both B2B and B2C transactions. This is leading to distrust between buyers and sellers, and the resulting cynicism could become an impediment to commerce. For sellers and marketplaces, this is also leading to reputational harm for their brands and the need for additional investments in intellectual property enforcement. In extreme cases, it has led to civil and criminal enforcement procedures. Technology solutions can reduce these risks by addressing key elements of trust in business transactions, such as:

- Authenticating the validity of the party, which may include their identity.
- Ensuring the authenticity of financial transactions — make sure the money is real, and that it goes where it is supposed to, when it is supposed to.
- Preventing errors and fraud, from double spending to theft.
- Ensuring the authenticity of products and services.
- Preventing disclosure of sensitive information to unauthorized parties.

Blockchain solutions can address many of these elements of trust, but they typically need to be combined with physical security and authentication technologies in order to be effective.[7] ~

ENDNOTES

1. Source: https://www.cnbc.com/2019/07/10/billion-dollar-natural-disasters-rising-these-states-better-prepare.html
2. Source: https://www.foreignaffairs.com/articles/world/2019-02-12/broken-bargain
3. Source: https://www.sciencedirect.com/science/article/abs/pii/S0016328716302063
4. Source: https://www.bloomberg.com/news/articles/2019-10-12/is-the-world-economy-sliding-into-first-recession-since-2009
5. Source: https://www.zdnet.com/article/the-scariest-hacks-and-vulnerabilities-of-2019/
6. Source: https://newsroom.ibm.com/2019-10-08-New-IBM-Sterling-Supply-Chain-Suite-Takes-Aim-at-50-Billion-Market-by-Helping-Clients-Reduce-Costs-and-Untangle-the-Complexities-of-Their-Global-Supply-Chains
7. Source: https://www.ledgerinsights.com/honeywell-blockchain-aircraft-parts/

Daniel Stanton is a supply chain entrepreneur, the best-selling author of *Supply Chain Management For Dummies*, and a popular LinkedIn Learning instructor.

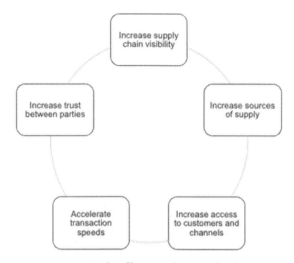

Automation's effect on the supply chain

Shipping containers from Asia arriving at the Port of Long Beach, California
Photo credit: Daniel Stanton (2019)

REMOTE WORK
AND AUTOMATION
Nawfal Patel and Jason Schenker

- The Futurist Institute -

While many futurists are focused on automation as computerized technological leverage for companies and workers, there has already been a major — and often overlooked — change in the way people work. And that's in remote work.

Simply put, remote working is not just a stopgap on the way to robotic process automation, even if it is a global flattening of workforce activities. Of course, this trend toward increased remote working has been going on for a number of years. But it is now at a tipping point. And, most interestingly, it is creating efficiencies — and benefits — for both workers and companies.

Remote work offers people more freedom and flexibility to live where and how they want. New technologies have made it easier for more and more people to live far from the office but still perform their job successfully. It is a trend poised to accelerate.

Currently, 54% of U.S. workers already work remotely at least once per month and 30% work remotely full time.[1] In the next year, the trend for remote work will continue to increase, with more companies offering opportunities for employees to live wherever they want as long as they get the job done.

Technology and automation are key to making long-distance work manageable for employees and freelancers. Digital tools can give remote workers access to whatever they need.

Since over 51% of the global population has internet access, there is some level of internet connectivity available in almost every corner of the world, so distant employees can always stay connected.[2] Platforms like Upwork and Fiver allow workers to advertise and offer their services to people around the globe while automating a lot of the small details, such as invoicing and marketing. This allows them to focus more on their work and not worry about the minutiae. Remote workers will seek to take advantage of new technologies and applications that allow them to be more efficient with their time outside of the office.

A remote working world is a billable hour world, where workers are also reviewed for their work, which leads to curation that favors the most effective workers. It is a world where everyone is more focused on their highest value tasks. This means that individuals — microentrepreneurs — will also be looking for technological leverage so they don't waste time on redundant mundane tasks. Even more than large corporations, individuals do not want to waste time if there are more efficient solutions available. And remote work is not just for low-level tasks.

There are attorneys, statisticians, economists, machine learning experts, and countless other high-dollar professionals that post for jobs on Upwork and other sites.

And an attorney, whether in an office or at the beach, does not want to waste time with accounting or scheduling minutiae. They will use applications to automate those kinds of tasks that add no value — and no revenue to their lives.

But this isn't just a dynamic for microentrepreneurs. It is also a big deal for major corporations. Because remote workers are more productive — and because remote work saves companies money.

A recent Global Workplace Analytics Costs & Benefits survey showed that teleworkers in some large companies are 35%-40% more productive than office workers doing the same job.[3] Another positive impact of allowing for telecommuting or remote work is the reduction of overhead costs for employers. Additionally, 60% of the companies in the survey claimed cost savings as a significant benefit from remote work, with IBM claiming to save $50 million in real estate costs alone.[4]

The increase of remote work could also have a big positive impact on smaller cities and towns. The cost of living in major cities is skyrocketing everywhere. Younger workers who want to live in cities are finding it increasingly difficult to find affordable housing. This has led to a small exodus of remote workers into smaller second- or third-tier cities and towns, where they can find higher quality living situations at affordable prices.

Companies are beginning to see the positive impact that remote workers can have, and they are starting to take serious notice by offering more flexible work arrangements to a significant number of employees.

However, not all aspects of remote work are positive. Maintaining a company's delicate balance of work efficiency and employee happiness will become even more difficult as more workers go remote. Employers have less visibility over their employees' actions, and they need to watch out for employees who try to take advantage of their newfound freedom. There are a lot more distractions while working outside of the office, and some employees can get easily sidetracked if not supervised.

Conversely, some remote workers find it difficult to maintain a good work/life balance. Since there is no physical separation between a remote employee's living space and their place of work, it can be hard for remote workers to fully disengage from their responsibilities and enjoy their free time. Also, remote workers have reported to feeling isolated from their co-workers.

These feelings can lead to lower morale and disconnected employees who don't form full relationships with each other. For employers, cybersecurity will become more critical as they allow people to work from remote locations. By spreading the work, the company is also increasing the attack surface and may be leaving itself exposed to bad actors due to one lax employee. These are just some of the reasons that remote work can be great. But they also underscore why remote work also needs to be managed properly to be effective and secure.

In the year ahead, more workers will seek remote opportunities and hope that the companies they want to work for will allow them to do so. Companies will have to make sure that they maintain efficiency and balance within their organization while still allowing workers to operate with a degree of autonomy.

This means that effective project management and maintaining communication will be critical for success. And those factors will only become more critical as ever-increasing numbers of workers seek out remote opportunities.

As we see more remote workers in the year ahead and beyond, we expect to see automated bots, AI solutions, and RPA that is specifically designed to help — and marketed to target — remote workers. This move in automation will make an increasingly distributed workforce more efficient, more effective, and more productive. ~

ENDNOTES

1. Source: http://owllabs.com/blog/remote-work-statistics
2. Source: https://qz.com/africa/1490997/more-than-half-of-worlds-population-using-the-internet-in-2018/
3. Source: https://globalworkplaceanalytics.com/resources/costs-benefits
4. Source: https://globalworkplaceanalytics.com/resources/costs-benefits

Nawfal Patel is the Operations Manager of The Futurist Institute and is currently traveling around the world while working remotely. He helped make this almanac become a reality while working in six different countries.

Jason Schenker is the Chairman of The Futurist Institute. He has worked remotely since 2007, both at McKinsey and Company as a Risk Specialist and running his own companies since 2009.

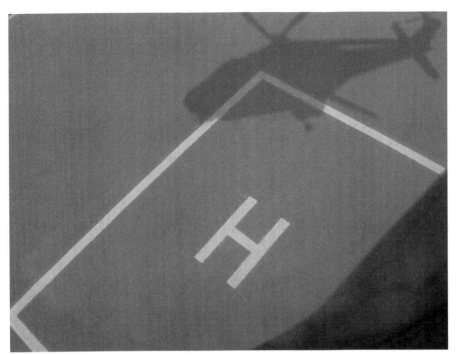

Remote Work.
Photo credit: Jason Schenker

THE FUTURIST INSTITUTE

 THE FUTURIST INSTITUTE

The Futurist Institute was founded in 2016 to help analysts, executives, and professionals incorporate new and emerging technology risk into their strategic planning. The Futurist Institute confers the Futurist and Long-Term Analyst™ (FLTA) designation and helps analysts become Certified Futurists™. Our courses have been approved for continuing education hours by the Certified Financial Planner Board of Standards (CFP Board), Global Association of Risk Professionals (GARP), and National Association of Certified Valuators and Analysts (NACVA).

Current Courses

The Future of Work
The Future of Data
The Future of Energy
The Future of Finance
The Future of Healthcare
The Future of Leadership
The Future of Transportation
Futurist Fundamentals
Quantum Computing

Visit The Futurist Institute:

www.futuristinstitute.org

ABOUT THE EDITOR

Jason Schenker is the Chairman of The Futurist Institute, the President of Prestige Economics, and the world's top-ranked financial market futurist. Bloomberg News has ranked Mr. Schenker the #1 forecaster in the world in 25 categories since 2011, including for his forecasts of crude oil prices, natural gas prices, the euro, the pound, the Swiss franc, the Chinese RMB, gold prices, industrial metals prices, agricultural prices, U.S. non-farm payrolls, and U.S. new home sales.

Mr. Schenker has written 18 books and edited three almanacs. Five of his books have been #1 Bestsellers on Amazon, including *Commodity Prices 101*, *Recession-Proof*, *Electing Recession*, *Quantum: Computing Nouveau*, and *Jobs for Robots*. He also edited the #1 Bestseller *The Robot and Automation Almanac — 2018* as well as the 2019 and 2020 editions of the almanac. Mr. Schenker is also a columnist for *Bloomberg Opinion*, and he has appeared as a guest host on Bloomberg Television as well as a guest on CNBC and other television media. He is frequently quoted in the press, including *The Wall Street Journal*, *The New York Times*, and *The Financial Times*.

Prior to founding Prestige Economics, Mr. Schenker worked for McKinsey & Company as a risk specialist, where he directed trading and risk initiatives on six continents. Before joining McKinsey, Mr. Schenker worked for Wachovia as an economist.

Mr. Schenker holds a Master's in Applied Economics from UNC Greensboro, a Master's in Negotiation from CSU Dominguez Hills, a Master's in German from UNC Chapel Hill, and a Bachelor's with distinction in History and German from The University of Virginia. He also holds a certificate in FinTech from MIT, an executive certificate in Supply Chain Management from MIT, a graduate certificate in Professional Development from UNC, a certificate in Negotiation from Harvard Law School, and a certificate in Cybersecurity from Carnegie Mellon University.

Mr. Schenker holds the professional designations ERP™ (Energy Risk Professional), CMT® (Chartered Market Technician), CVA® (Certified Valuation Analyst), CFP® (Certified Financial Planner), and FLTA™ (Certified Futurist and Long-Term Analyst). Mr. Schenker is also an instructor for LinkedIn Learning. His courses include Financial Risk Management, Recession-Proof Strategies, Audit and Due Diligence, and a weekly Economic Indicator Series.

Mr. Schenker is a member of the Texas Business Leadership Council, the only CEO-based public policy research organization in Texas, with a limited membership of 100 CEOs and Presidents. He is also a 2018 Board of Director member of the Texas Lyceum, a non-partisan, nonprofit that fosters business and policy dialogue on important U.S. and Texas issues. He is also the VP of Technology for the Texas Lyceum Executive Committee.

Mr. Schenker is an active executive in FinTech. He has been a member of the Central Texas Angel Network, and he advises multiple startups and nonprofits. He is also a member of the National Association of Corporate Directors as well as an NACD Board Governance Fellow.

In October 2016, Mr. Schenker founded The Futurist Institute to help consultants, strategists, and executives become futurists through an online and in-person training and certification program. Participants can earn the Certified Futurist and Long-Term Analyst™ — FLTA™ — designation.

Mr. Schenker was ranked one of the top 100 most influential financial advisors in the world by Investopedia in June 2018.

More information about Jason Schenker:
www.jasonschenker.com

More information about The Futurist Institute:
www.futuristinstitute.org

More information about Prestige Economics:
www.prestigeeconomics.com

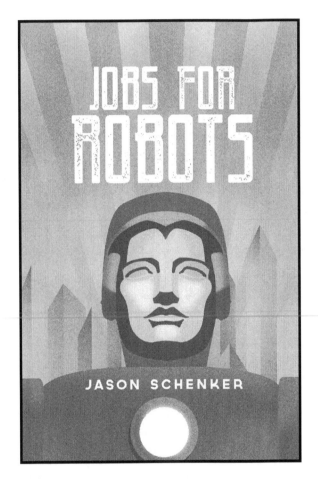

Jobs for Robots provides an in-depth look at the future of automation and robots, with a focus on the opportunities as well as the risks ahead. Job creation in coming years will be extremely strong for the kind of workers that do not require payroll taxes, health care, or vacation: robots. *Jobs for Robots* was published in February 2017. This book has been a #1 Best Seller on Amazon.

ABOUT THE PUBLISHER

Prestige Professional Publishing was founded in 2011 to produce insightful and timely professional reference books. We are registered with the Library of Congress.

Published Titles

Be the Shredder, Not the Shred
Commodity Prices 101
Electing Recession
Financial Risk Management Fundamentals
Futureproof Supply Chain
A Gentle Introduction to Audit and Due Diligence
Jobs for Robots
Midterm Economics
Quantum: Computing Nouveau
Reading the Economic Tea Leaves
Robot-Proof Yourself
Spikes: Growth Hacking Leadership
The Dumpster Fire Election
The Fog of Data
The Future of Energy
The Future of Finance is Now
The Promise of Blockchain
The Robot and Automation Almanac — 2018
The Robot and Automation Almanac — 2019
The Robot and Automation Almanac — 2020

Future Titles

The Future of Agriculture
The Future of Healthcare

DISCLAIMER

FROM THE PUBLISHER

The following disclaimer applies to any content in this book:

This book is commentary intended for general information use only and is not investment advice. Prestige Professional Publishing LLC does not make recommendations on any specific or general investments, investment types, asset classes, unregulated markets, specific equities, bonds, or other investment vehicles. Prestige Professional Publishing LLC does not guarantee the completeness or accuracy of analyses and statements in this book, nor does Prestige Professional Publishing LLC assume any liability for any losses that may result from the reliance by any person or entity on this information. Opinions, forecasts, and information are subject to change without notice. This book does not represent a solicitation or offer of financial or advisory services or products; this book is only market commentary intended and written for general information use only. This book does not constitute investment advice.

DISCLAIMER

FROM THE FUTURIST INSTITUTE

The following disclaimer applies to any content in this book:

This book is commentary intended for general information use only and is not investment advice. The Futurist Institute does not make recommendations on any specific or general investments, investment types, asset classes, non-regulated markets, specific equities, bonds, or other investment vehicles. The Futurist Institute does not guarantee the completeness or accuracy of analyses and statements in this book, nor does The Futurist Institute assume any liability for any losses that may result from the reliance by any person or entity on this information. Opinions, forecasts, and information are subject to change without notice. This book does not represent a solicitation or offer of financial or advisory services or products, and are market commentary intended and written for general information use only. This book does not constitute investment advice.

FI THE FUTURIST INSTITUTE

Copyright © 2019 Prestige Professional Publishing LLC

THE ROBOT AND AUTOMATION ALMANAC - 2020

COMPILED BY THE FUTURIST INSTITUTE

EDITED BY JASON SCHENKER

ISBN: 978-1-946197-37-5 *Paperback*
      978-1-946197-36-8 *Ebook*

Made in the USA
Lexington, KY
27 November 2019